INTERNATIONAL TRADE, FOREIGN DIRECT INVESTMENT AND THE ECONOMIC ENVIRONMENT

Also by P. K. M. Tharakan

COMPETITIVENESS OF EUROPEAN INDUSTRY (*editor with A. Francis*)

IMPERFECT COMPETITION AND INTERNATIONAL TRADE (*editor with D. Greenaway*)

INTRA-INDUSTRY TRADE: Theory, Evidence and Extensions (*editor with J. Kol*)

POLICY IMPLICATIONS OF ANTI-DUMPING MEASURES (*editor*)

Also by D. Van Den Bulcke

CHANGING ECONOMIC ORDER (*editor with J. van den Broeck*)

EUROPEAN HEADQUARTERS OF AMERICAN MULTINATIONAL COMPANIES IN BELGIUM AND BRUSSELS

INVESTMENT AND DIVESTMENT POLICIES OF MULTINATIONAL COMPANIES IN EUROPE

RECENT TRENDS IN INTERNATIONAL DEVELOPMENT (*editor*)

International Trade, Foreign Direct Investment and the Economic Environment

Essays in Honour of Professor Sylvain Plasschaert

Edited by

P. K. M. Tharakan
Professor of Economics
Faculty of Applied Economics, and Centre for Development Studies
University of Antwerp – UFSIA
Belgium

and

D. Van Den Bulcke
Professor of International Management and Development
Institute of Development Policy and Management
University of Antwerp – RUCA
Belgium

First published in Great Britain 1998 by
MACMILLAN PRESS LTD
Houndmills, Basingstoke, Hampshire RG21 6XS and London
Companies and representatives throughout the world

A catalogue record for this book is available from the British Library.

ISBN 0–333–65797–7

First published in the United States of America 1998 by
ST. MARTIN'S PRESS, INC.,
Scholarly and Reference Division,
175 Fifth Avenue, New York, N.Y. 10010

ISBN 0–312–17536–1

Library of Congress Cataloging-in-Publication Data
International trade, foreign direct investment, and the economic environment.
p. cm.
"Papers . . . presented to a symposium held at the University of Antwerp in honour of . . . Professor Sylvain Plasschaert"—Pref.
Includes bibliographical references and index.
ISBN 0–312–17536–1 (cloth)
1. International trade—Congresses. 2. Investments, Foreign–
–Congresses. 3. International economic relations—Congresses.
I. Tharakan, P. K. Mathew. II. Bulcke, D. van den.
III. Plasschaert, Sylvain R. F.
HF1372.I584 1997
382—dc21 97–9649
CIP

---

10 9 8 7 6 5 4 3 2 1
07 06 05 04 03 02 01 00 99 98

Printed in Great Britain by
The Ipswich Book Company Ltd
Ipswich, Suffolk

Contents

List of Tables

List of Figures

List of Exhibits

Notes on the Contributors

Lodewijk Berlage is Professor at the University of Leuven (KUL).

Jacques Drèze is Professor Emeritus at the University of Louvain (UCL).

John Dunning is Professor at the University of Reading and the University of Rutgers.

Herbert Glesjer is Professor at the University of Namur (FUNDP) and the Free University of Brussels (VUB).

Birgit Kerstens is Research Assistant at the University of Antwerp - UFSIA.

Sanjaya Lall is Fellow at the University of Oxford, Queen Elisabeth House.

Theo Peeters is Professor at the University of Leuven (KUL)

Bernard Snoy is Director for the Belgian, Luxemburgian and Slovenian constituencies at the European Bank for Reconstruction and Development.

P.K. Mathew Tharakan is Professor at the University of Antwerp - UFSIA and RUCA and Visiting Professor at the University of Louvain (UCL).

Danny Van Den Bulcke is Professor at the University of Antwerp - RUCA and UFSIA and President of the Institute of Development Policy and Management.

Sophie Vandermeulen is Research Assistant at the University of Leuven (KUL).

Willy Van Ryckeghem is Senior Regional Economic Advisor at the Inter American Development Bank in Washington, DC.

Haiyan Zhang is Ph.D. student at the University of Antwerp -RUCA

Preface

International trade and foreign direct investment (FDI) are among the frontier areas of research in economics. The interest evoked by these topics is partly due to their policy relevance. The rapid growth in international trade and FDI in recent years has clearly augmented their importance to policy considerations.

The papers contained in this volume were presented to a symposium held at the University of Antwerp in honour of an internationally known expert in these fields - Professor Sylvain Plasschaert. The organization of the symposium was a joint venture of the Centre of Development Studies and the Institute of Development Policy and Management of the University of Antwerp, with the support of the National Fund for Scientific Research. Professor Plasschaert's work in academic and advisory capacity took him to different parts of the world, brought him into contact with people and institutions shaping the development of international flows of trade and investment. From this experience and from his own academic research he developed a remarkable capacity for identifying issues that are crucial from a policy perspective. That, in turn, has remained the hallmark of his own contributions in these areas and influenced the structure of this volume.

The first part (Chapters 1 to 4) of this volume deals with international trade issues. It treats topics such as the role of import constraints in the growth of Sub-Saharan countries; the effects of prices on the trade between members of a common market and the danger of protectionist misuse of the anti-dumping mechanisms.

The second part (Chapters 5 to 8) of the volume deals with foreign direct investment issues. The importance of domestic policy variables in attracting FDI; the relationship between the emerging global economy, national governments and supernational economic regimes; the changing perceptions of FDI in development; and foreign equity joint ventures in China, are the topics treated in that part.

Professor Plasschaert's longstanding interest in developing countries and development problems as testified by his directorship of the Centre for Development Studies of the University of Antwerp; his internationally acknowledged work on multinational companies; and his ongoing work on the Chinese economy; are all directly or indirectly reflected in these contributions.

As his well-known work on fiscal federalism, and centrally planned economy shows, Plasschaert has also maintained considerable interest on a number of issues which characterize the international economic environment within which trade and investment take place. The contributions in the third part of this volume (Chapters 9 to 11), dealing with devolution in the European Union; the transition of the former centrally planned economies to market-oriented ones; and the problems raised by the move towards the European Monetary Union, reflect this interest.

We would like to express our thanks to all the contributors for their participation in the symposium in honour of Professor Sylvain Plasschaert. We are also grateful to them for the co-operation they extended to us in the preparation of this volume.

The production of the typescript was undertaken by Ms. Patricia Franck who displayed enormous patience in incorporating numerous changes in the text. We are happy to record here our appreciation of her patience and efficiency.

P.K.Mathew Tharakan
University of Antwerp - UFSIA

Danny Van Den Bulcke
University of Antwerp - RUCA

List of Abbreviations

AD/CVD	Antidumping/Countervailing Duty
AD	Antidumping
BOT	Build-Operate-Transfer
BOO	Build-Own-Operate
CADIC	Comparative Analysis of the Domestic Industry Condition
CEE	Central and Eastern Europe
CEPS	Center for European Policy Studies
CG	Consultive Group
CN	Customs Nomenclature
CON	Concentration (variable)
CPEs	Central Planned Economies
CVD	Countervailing Duties
EBRD	European Bank for Reconstruction and Development
EC	European Community
EFF	Extended Fund Facility
EMU	Economic and Monetary Union
ESAF	Enhanced Structural Adjustment Facility
ESCB	European System of Central Banks
EU	European Union
FDI	Foreign Direct Investment
FHN	Finger, Hall and Nelson
FIFO	First In, First Out
FRE	Federated Regions of Europe
FSU	Former Soviet Union
GATT	General Agreement on Tariffs and Trade
GDI	Gross Domestic Investment
GDP	Gross Domestic Product
HITEC	High Technology
IBRD	International Bank for Reconstruction and Development
IDB	International Development Bank
IFC	International Finance Corporation
IMEU	Injury Margin of the European Union
IMF	International Monetary Fund
ITC	International Trade Commission
JVs	Joint Ventures
MNEs	Multinational Enterprises
MFA	Multi-Fibre Agreement
NACE	Nomenclature d'Activités de la Communauté Européenne

NAFTA	North American Free Trade Area
NIEs	Newly Industrialized Economies
NPC	Nord-Pas-de-Calais
NTBs	Non-Tariff Barriers
OECD	Organization of Economic Cooperation and Development
OLS	Ordinary Least Squares
PHARE	Poland-Hungary Assistance for the Reconstruction of the Economy
RTGS	Real-Time Gross Settlement Systems
SALs	Structural Adjustment Loans
SDR	Special Draining Rights
SITC	Standard International Trade Classification
SRE	Status of Region of Europe
SSA	Sub-saharan Africa
STF	Systemic Transformation Facility
TACIS	Technical Assistance Community of Independent States
TNCs	Transnational Corporations
UN	United Nations
UNCTAD	United Nations Conference on Trade and Development
UNCTC	United Nations Centre on Transnational Corporations
UNDP	United Nations Development Programme
WEU	Western European Union
WTO	World Trade Organisation

1 International Trade, Foreign Direct Investment and the Economic Environment

P.K. Mathew Tharakan and
Danny Van Den Bulcke

1.1 INTRODUCTION

The rapid growth of international trade and foreign direct investments in recent years have helped to focus the attention of economists on these and a number of related issues. Some of such topics are of a theoretical nature, others have more empirical content. In the present volume, we have included a set of contributions dealing with topics of the latter type. Their policy relevance is self-evident.

While unanimity about the importance of topics in this vast field is unlikely, there can be no doubt that a number of issues dealt with here are obvious candidates for consideration. For example we know that the rapid growth of some economies has been trade-driven. Is it then likely that the lack of success of some others, has been due to import constraints? Can comparative costs explain the steep growth of trade between certain industrial countries? What is the specific nature of the problems raised by the increasing use of contingent protection, particularly the antidumping mechanism?

Foreign direct investment provides an equally fertile field for empirical investigation. How important are domestic policy variables in attracting foreign direct investments? What has been the experience of Latin America? Of China? If markets are essentially efficient and the transnational corporations represent the most developed forms of market efficiency, can such corporations be considered as the new custodians of development?

In addition to such topics dealing directly with international trade and foreign direct investment, there are a number of issues which characterise the international economic environment within which such trade and investment take place. The move towards devolution under way in some countries, the transition of the former centrally planned economies to market-oriented ones, the problems raised by the move towards the European Monetary Union, these are all issues which deserve analytical attention.

1.2 INTERNATIONAL TRADE ISSUES

The remarkable rate of growth achieved by the East Asian economies and the central role played by international trade in that growth have inevitably influenced the type of questions raised about the deteriorating economic performance of Sub-Saharan Africa (SSA). In addressing that problem in Chapter 2, Berlage and Vandermeulen distinguish between fundamental and immediate causes. Among the fundamental causes often mentioned are the political structures of pre-colonial African societies, their colonial heritage and the nature of contemporaneous African states. The immediate causes include the loss of SSA's share in world markets, the debt burden, the over-regulation of economic activity and the ensuing disincentives for the private sector. Berlage and Vandermeulen investigate empirically whether imports have constituted a constraint on the growth of individual Sub-Saharan countries. This is done by using a switching regression model in which GDP growth is 'normally' determined by the supply of labour and capital and by changes in efficiency which result from increased exports, but might be on the other hand constrained by the availability of imports. The econometric exercise makes use of data pertaining to fifteen of the most populated SSA countries. For the purpose of the present analysis, the crucial explanatory variable in the specification which attempts to explain changes in the gross domestic product at constant prices is the imports of intermediate inputs.

The test yielded mixed results. For some countries the estimated coefficient of the import variable was greater than one, for some other countries the value of the coefficient was not significantly greater than one, and there were countries for which the coefficient was not significantly different from zero or was even negative. There was good to weak evidence for the existence of an import constraint for six SSA countries and for those countries the computed probability of an import constrained regime was higher during the 1970s and 1980s than during the 1960s. For one country, i.e. Kenya, imports did not constrain growth in most years. For the remaining countries, the statistical results were too poor to allow any conclusion. The authors ascribe the limited nature of the evidence on import constrained growth to methodological and data-related problems. The question of course remains whether the fundamental causes they have identified, but not investigated, have played a major role in the economic deterioration of Sub-Saharan Africa.

An important literature exists on the effects of economic integration already. Yet the use of detailed price data for such analyses is still rather rare. There are different reasons for this. Unit export- or import-price data developed from trade statistics tend to yield poor results in econometric analyses partly because of the heterogeneity of the trade classification. But detailed consumer price data collected by the statistical office of the European Community (EC) in various member countries, and covering a long period of time do exist. In Chapter 3, Herbert Glejser makes use of such data to test the effect of prices on trade during the first twelve years of the European Community.

Glejser uses the price and trade data for two purposes. First he carries out a test of the comparative cost theory in which pre-common market prices are assumed to play the role of pretrade prices. Secondly he analyzes the effects of the variation of trade on the change in price disparities.

On the basis of the results obtained for 21 regressions, Glejser concludes that in spite of the alternative theories which have gained prominence in recent years, Ricardo's comparative costs theory remains a very useful tool in explaining the trade flows between industrialized countries. But he also finds evidence which suggests that non-economic factors play a role in the determination of trade flows.

The second part of Glejser's analysis suggests that the trade expansion between the member countries of the EC often contributed to the narrowing down of the price discrepancies between them, in spite of the high supply elasticities that existed during the boom period covered by the study. He concludes that the demand elasticities must have been very high too and suggests that earlier studies must have underestimated the welfare effects of the EC during the 1960s by using low values of elasticities.

During the post-World War II years, remarkable success has been achieved in obtaining widespread reduction of tariff protection. More recently, some progress has been made also in reaching agreements on dismantling some forms of non-tariff barriers (NTBs). But a number of economists have expressed the concern that during the same period, the leading members of the World Trade Organisation (WTO) are increasingly using certain forms of contingent protection, particularly the antidumping (AD) regulations for import impeding purposes. In Chapter 3, Tharakan and Kerstens analyse the antidumping policy of the European Union (EU).

The authors point out some of the ambiguities contained in the antidumping regulations in general and those which are specific to the EU in particular. These in fact provide the loopholes which can be used to divert this corrective mechanism for protectionist purposes. Whether such a misuse of the AD mechanism in fact takes place or not is of course an empirical question. On the basis of the general analysis and the review of the available empirical evidence, the authors suggest that the injury determination process is particularly amenable to misuse and that cases having certain industry-country characteristics are especially vulnerable.

The most fundamental problem with the injury determination process used in the EU is that it does not tell us what the margin of injury would have been if there were no dumping. Yet, some parties to the cases decided at the U.S. International Trade Commission (ITC), are increasingly making use of a counterfactual analysis contained in the so-called CADIC (Comparative Analysis of the Domestic Industry Condition) model to simulate the margin of injury. Tharakan and Kerstens use the CADIC model to make alternative estimates of injury margin for a large number of cases decided by the EU. Their results show that the EU has been systematically overestimating the margin of injury in the antidumping cases. The authors then measure the differences between the injury margin estimated by the EU and those obtained by the CADIC model, and carry out a regression analysis to identify the major explanation for such differences. They find that in the case of technology intensive industries, cases where Japanese firms, or firms from centrally planned economies are involved, EU's overestimation of injury margins tend to be higher. They conclude by arguing for a reform of the injury determination mechanisms of the EU.

1.3 FOREIGN DIRECT INVESTMENT ISSUES

The importance of domestic policy variables in attracting foreign direct investment (FDI) inflows is often stressed in policy discussions, but rarely subjected to rigorous analysis. In Chapter 5, Van Ryckeghem uses stepwise pooled regression techniques to test the validity of the above-mentioned hypothesis for the seven largest Latin American economies during the period 1970-1992.

The starting point of the research is a basic hypothesis about the existence of a foreign investment accelerator which supposes a relationship between the FDI/GDP ratio and the immediately past growth rate of the real GDP of the host country. In the ensuing econometric analysis the author attempts to establish the difference which macro-economic policies make to foreign direct investment by first estimating a function without policy variables, and next a function incorporating such variables.

The specification without the policy variable confirms the existence of an FDI accelerator as well as the presence of a positive scale factor, the latter reflecting the fact that large economies tend to receive proportionately more foreign investment. An expanded specification which incorporates policy variables yields interesting results which answer the central question raised by the study. The results show that import liberalization, depreciation of the real effective exchange rate and deficit reduction have a significant impact on FDI. As Van Ryckeghem points out, while the results themselves do not come as a surprise, their importance consists of the quantification of the effects of these policy variables made possible by the exercise. They make it possible to carry out simulations of the outcomes of policy options which should be of use to those who are interested in ways and means for attracting foreign direct investment flows to Latin American countries.

In Chapter 6 Dunning starts with the sometimes disputed assumption of the advent of a global economy. The term connotates an economy in which there is a close economic interdependence among and between the leading nations in trade, investment and cooperative commercial relationships and where there is a relatively free cross-border flow of people, assets, goods or services. Such a global economy, the author argues, is requiring national governments to reappraise their domestic macro-organizational policies and to take a more systematic approach to the implementation of these policies. It is also pointed out that the globalization of the economy requires the governments to take a more constructive and coordinated action to help cross-border markets to work more efficiently.

The author is careful to clarify that these propositions do not mean that there should be necessarily less government intervention or that the governments should intervene more in the decision making process of business enterprises. But what is required is the acknowledgement, on the part of the governments, that markets are not a free good and that they cost resources to set up, operate and maintain. Further, the efficiency of many markets, particulary those which function in a global environment, is not solely determined by the transaction of the buyers and sellers in those markets. A number of other factors including the actions taken by other governments determine the degree of efficiency of such markets. This being the case, the governments should, according to Dunning, reexamine their organizational structures and administrative regimes in order to concentrate on only those activities which, relative to the private sector, they are best able to undertake. He also argues that supra-national regimes like the World Bank, the GATT and the IMF will have to reexamine their role if the competition between countries to attract greater shares of FDI is not to lead to distortions.

As Lall makes clear in Chapter 7, the neo-liberal faith in the central role of transnational corporations (TNCs) in international development is not shared by all. There are voices urging caution and they deserve to be heard.

As Lall points out, the global shift of policy to market orientation and liberal economic regimes has swept aside many of the reservations which formerly characterised the attitudes towards inward FDI. There is the growing belief that markets are essentially efficient and as the TNCs represent the most developed form of market efficiency, they are now being proposed in many influential circles as the best way for the developing host countries to maximize their static or dynamic economic benefits. But, Lall argues that the earlier questions about the effects of TNCs cannot be simply ignored. Within developing countries there are evident market failures. This reality, combined with the fact that the TNCs are the result of imperfect international markets for intangible assets means that the imposition of internalized TNC markets on the deficient markets of developing countries can lead to ambiguous results.

In developing this line of argument, Lall examines the experience of some of the fast growing East Asian economies and the policies they adopted towards the TNCs, and compares them with the example of Chile. He feels that these examples yield some useful lessons about effective interventions which can be undertaken by governments. These include providing favours only in return for performance and the setting up of institutional mechanisms for regular and intense consultations between officials and business. The essence of the message is that instead of viewing the TNCs as the 'new custodians of development', the host countries would be well-advised to undertake some careful interventions to promote the development of local enterprise and capabilities within a fairly welcoming regime for FDI.

FDI flows to China have risen so sharply in recent years that China is now second only to the United States as a host country to such investments. This, combined with the fact that there have been frequent adaptations in the Chinese policy towards foreign direct investment since the end of 1970s makes it an interesting case for the study of the dynamic interaction between national policy measures and TNC strategies. The analysis of the Chinese experience reported in Chapter 8 by Van Den Bulcke and Zhang yields some interesting insights on this question.

Van Den Bulcke and Zhang point out that the response of the TNCs vis-à-vis the Chinese FDI regulations varied according to the latter's firm specific advantage and strategic positioning. Faced with the high barrier against exports to China, the TNCs from the Western industrialised countries used the 'tariff wall jumping strategy' of inward investments, which in the classic mould of such import-substituting investment, turned out to be capital- and human-capital intensive. But the firms from some of the newly industrialised countries, especially Taiwan and Hong Kong carried out labour-intensive, export oriented investments in China. The investors from some of the Asian developing countries were mainly present in the processing of raw materials and agricultural activities in China.

The ownership structure of the foreign investment in China seems to have been determined not only by the financial capabilities of the investors, but also by their need to acquire local market knowledge. During the period of the import-substituting investments, the western TNCs preferred equity joint ventures with local partners, rather than wholly owned subsidiaries, because they were concerned with the accessibility to domestic market information and good relationship with the local government. With the extension and the development of market mechanism in China in the 1980s, the dependence on the government and the involvement with the Chinese partners lessened.

The labour intensive export oriented and the resource seeking FDI coming mainly from the neighbouring economies were most often owned and controlled by 'overseas Chinese'. The fact that they had better personal contacts, family connections, political links, etc. in China, was probably one of the reasons why their equity stakes were lower than that of the western firms.

Within the context of the increasing liberalization of national economies, TNCs tend to have more and more locational alternatives to efficiently organize their global business network. Van Den Bulcke and Zhang remark that this raises some challenges to the Chinese government policy with respect to FDI.

1.4 INTERNATIONAL ECONOMIC ENVIRONMENT ISSUES

International trade and investment take place in, and are influenced by an environment characterised by certain specific important problems. Among such problems which mark the broad political-economic landscape of Europe in the closing years of the 20th century three specific issues stand out: the tendency towards some form of regionalism or devolution of existing political entities; the transition of the erstwhile centrally planned economies of Central and Eastern Europe and the former Soviet Union towards competitive ones; and the progress towards an European Monetary Union. Some aspects of these topics are treated in Chapters 9-11.

The scenario in which a geographical area, currently part of the territory of a Member State of the European Union could henceforth belong to the Union directly without being any longer part of the Member State (i.e. having the 'status of Region of Europe') has been the subject of sometimes intense, and often emotional discussions in certain countries. In Chapter 9 Drèze attempts to place that discussion on a technical footing. As he points out at the outset, his purpose is limited to defining the concept of the 'Status of Region of Europe' (SRE) and discussing the conditions under which its implementation could be Pareto-improving.

If a region of a Member state of the EU were to become a 'Region of Europe', it would hope to reap some benefits of an allocative nature by formulating public activities or policies more closely related to the local needs and means and to local preferences, and by controlling more tightly activities for which it becomes financially responsible. These benefits should be matched against the costs of collective decision making at the appropriate levels of (de)centralization. Whether the move to become an SRE is desirable or not, depends on the balance of these costs and benefits.

Drèze goes on to point out that the move would also have distributive implications if there existed net transfers between the Region and the Member State to which it belonged but argues that these lump sum transfers should not affect the decisions, if it is to be guided by a criterion of Pareto improvement. The viewpoint that is emerging from the analysis is that there is room for 'Regions of Europe' within a 'Europe of Nations' and that there is no overriding reason why a move towards a 'Europe of Regions' should proceed synchronously over the whole territory of the EU.

The process in which the politically fragile countries of Central and Eastern Europe (CEE) and the Former Soviet Union (FSU) face the daunting challenge of moving from centrally planned economies to competitive ones is, in many ways an instructive one. This process has also moved the Bretton Woods institutions, created fifty years ago, to facilitate monetary cooperation and promote economic development, closer to their original vision of becoming global institutions. In Chapter 10, Snoy focuses attention on what we have learned from the historical transition under way in the CEE and the FSU and the specific contributions of the International Monetary Fund and the World Bank Group.

Snoy states that everyone, including the Bretton Woods institutions, underestimated the difficulty of the transition process and the magnitude of the transition recession. While the usefulness of the various programmes of the Bank in coping with the problems raised by the transition process is not in doubt, the question remains whether the Bretton Woods institutions could have moved more quickly and provided more resources.

Institution building is probably the most important aspect of a successful transition strategy. Although this is not a primary mandate of the Bretton Woods institutions, they have helped to bring about substantial technical assistance for this purpose. They have also insisted on the crucial role of incomes policies, fiscal reform and the creation of social safety nets in their stabilization programmes and policy-based lending. Besides the World Bank has focused its human and financial resources on solving the combined problems of governance, restructuring and privatization of the major state-owned enterprises, and banking reform. The Bretton Woods institutions have even helped to catalyse international financial flows to the CEE although some questions remain as to the adequacy of the present efforts for some of the less privileged FSU countries.

A heated debate has raged in Europe in recent years over the criteria and timetable concerning Economic and Monetary Union (EMU). Nevertheless, there is little doubt that EMU is bound to become a reality even if some modifications to the Maastricht 'guidelines' have to be accepted. Higher efficiency and transparency in European payment systems are of course an apparent aspect of the move towards EMU. In Chapter 11, Peeters looks at the problems of cross-border payment systems and the European Monetary Union.

Small-value cross-border payments in Europe are a major concern to consumers and consumer organizations. The European Commission has undertaken initiatives to achieve eventually the objectives of making cross-border transfers as quick and efficient as transfers within one and the same member state, and to eliminate double charging. But the main problem is that cross-border transactions rarely benefit from the cross-subsidization and cost-sharing features that are common practices in domestic payments. Because of this, it is expected that charges for cross-border retail payments will continue to exceed those for domestic retail payments for a long time to come.

National central banks are specially concerned about the question of risk control and risk reduction in large-value cross-border payments. In accordance with the principle of decentralization, the large-value payment system for stage III of EMU will be composed of a real time gross settlement system in each member state with the interlinking of these facilities to process cross-border payments. But at the same time correspondent banking arrangements and net settlement systems will continue to co-exist. But as Peeters points out, the linkages between a centralized monetary policy in EMU and a decentralized supervision of the payment systems can lead to some conflicts, particularly in crisis situations.

2 Have Imports Constrained Economic Growth in Sub-Saharan Africa?

Lodewijk Berlage and
Sophie Vandermeulen[1]

2.1 INTRODUCTION

During the period 1961-1973 gross domestic product (GDP) of Sub-Saharan Africa (SSA) grew at an average annual rate of 4.6%. Between 1973 and 1980 the annual growth rate fell to an average of 2.7%. In the eighties there was a further slow-down: the average annual growth rate was only 2% (2.5% if Nigeria is excluded) whereas population increased at an annual rate of 3.1%; per capita income therefore declined.[2] When trying to explain the deteriorating economic performance of SSA, one can distinguish between fundamental and immediate causes. Among the former are the political structure of pre-colonial African societies, the colonial heritage and the nature of contemporaneous African states (Cockcroft, 1990). Among the immediate causes of the deterioration are the unfavourable external environment, the loss of SSA's share in world markets, the debt burden, government deficits, overregulation of economic activity and the ensuing disincentives for the private sector, in particular for agriculture.[3]

One particular explanation of SSA's weak economic performance, which has frequently been mentioned in the literature (Helleiner, 1986 and 1992; Ravenhill, 1986; Killick, 1992; World Bank and UNDP, 1989) is the existence of an import constraint. GDP growth, so the argument goes, was critically affected by a shortage of imported inputs, itself the result of a foreign exchange shortage. The latter had its origin in some of the immediate causes of the economic decline just mentioned. Due to the evolution of the markets for the typical African export products, to policies which resulted in a loss of SSA's market shares, and, for some countries, to a reduced access to foreign finance, the volume of the available foreign exchange stagnated or declined. In addition, an increasing fraction of this volume was needed to serve the region's foreign debt. As a result the import capacity of most Sub-Saharan African countries stagnated or increased only slowly. SSA needs imports of intermediate and investment goods to support its production and to maintain and extend its capital stock; in the short run at least some of these imports cannot be substituted for by domestic production. In this view therefore, growth was import constrained.

The purpose of this chapter is to investigate empirically whether imports have constituted a constraint on the growth of individual Sub-Saharan countries. The origin of the import constraint is not analysed.[4] We use a switching regression model, in which GDP growth is 'normally' determined by the supply of labour and capital and by changes in efficiency, which result from increased exports, but might on the other hand be constrained by the available imports. The model is presented in section 2.2. In section 2.3 the regression model is specified and the data are described. In section 2.4 the regression results are analysed. Conclusions are formulated in section 2.5.

2.2 THE MODEL

We start out with a neoclassical production function. GDP depends on the labour force, L_t, and on the capital stock, K_t. In addition the export volume, X_t, is included in the production function based on the assumption that marginal efficiency of production factors is higher in the export sector than in the rest of the economy.[5]

$$Yt = f(L_t, K_t, X_t) \qquad [1]$$

where Y_t = gross domestic product at constant prices.
Differentiation of (1) yields

$$DY_t = f_L DL_t + f_K DK_t + f_X DX_t \qquad [2]$$

where $Dx_t = x_t - x_{t-1}$. The symbols f_L and f_K stand for the marginal product of labour and capital; f_L will be zero if there is surplus labour. f_X is the marginal increase in productivity derived from higher activity in the export sector. If factor productivity in this sector does not differ from that in the rest of the economy, f_X will be zero.

It is assumed that, in addition to labour and capital, production requires non-substitutable imported inputs. Alternatively substitution of some imported inputs may be possible in the long run, but not in the short run, say within the time span of a few years. Assuming that the relation between output and non-substitutable inputs is linear, we can write were $$bY_t \leq M_{it} \qquad [3]$$

were M_i stands for imports of intermediate goods. Relation (3) states that in order to produce one unit of output at least b units of imports are needed. If there is no shortage of foreign exchange, imported inputs will be equal to or higher than bY and the causality in (3) will run from left to right. If however such a shortage exists, (3) will hold with equality and the causality will run from right to left.

As data on imports of intermediate goods are not readily available, we establish a relation between output and total imports. For this purpose, assume that imports of intermediate goods cannot be higher than a fraction f of total imports:

$$M_{it} \leq fM_t \qquad [4]$$

In the absence of a shortage of foreign exchange, imports other than those of intermediate goods can be relatively abundant. But if there is a shortage of foreign exchange, such imports are compressed to their strict minimum and (4) will hold with equality.

Combining relations (3) and (4), both with equality, yields for the case of a foreign exchange shortage

$$Y_t = (f/b)M_t = aM_t \qquad [5]$$

Remark that the parameters b and f are both less than one. However one may expect that for a low income economy as a whole, as opposed to individual sectors, the value of the parameter b will be rather low. Therefore it seems reasonable to expect a to be greater than one.

Writing (5) in differential form yields

$$DY_t = aDM_t \qquad [6]$$

We have now two relations to explain an observed change in GDP, (2) and (6). In what follows we call these regime 1 and regime 2. Write the change in GDP, as determined by the former, as DY_{t1} and as defined by the latter as DY_{t2}. The observed change in GDP will then be the smaller of the two expressions:

$$DY_t = min(DY_{t1}, DY_{t2}) \qquad [7]$$

If there is no foreign exchange constraint imports are likely to be larger than strictly required and the minimum will be reached for DY_{t1}. In the presence of such a constraint, growth will be determined by available imports and the minimum reached for DY_{t2}.

2.3 ECONOMETRIC SPECIFICATION AND DATA

For the purpose of estimation, relations (2), (6) and (7) are reformulated as follows:

$$
\begin{aligned}
DY_{t1} &= a_0 + a_1 DL_t + a_2 DK_t + a_3 DX_t + u_{1t} \\
DY_{t2} &= b_0 + b_1 DM_t + u_{2t} \qquad [8] \\
Y_t &= min\ (DY_{t1}, DY_{t2})
\end{aligned}
$$

where u_1 and u_2 are assumed to be independently, normally distributed error terms with zero means and variances $(\tilde{O}_1)^2$ and $(\tilde{O}_2)^2$, serially independent and not correlated with each other.

(8) is known as the switching regression model, pioneered by Maddala and Nelson (1974) and described e.g. in Maddala (1986). For its estimation the maximum likelihood function is specified and maximized.

In order to verify whether the economic growth of SSA countries has indeed been constrained by imports, (8) was estimated assuming that the sample separation is unknown. It is known that this approach is asking a lot from the data and that therefore 'the results cannot normally be expected to be very good' (Maddala, 1986, p.1642). However as our first interest is to test for the existence of an import constraint rather than to obtain efficient estimates of the coefficients, it would not make sense to determine a priori the sample separation, i.e. to determine the regime to which each observation belongs on the basis of information outside of the sample.

Equation (8) has been estimated on the basis of data for fifteen countries of Sub-Saharan Africa with a 1989 population of at least 7 million and for the years 1960–89. Estimation of a switching regression model requires sufficiently long time series; 30 observations are sometimes mentioned as a strict minimum. We have 29 observations per country.[6] Countries with civil wars during the period under consideration (Ethiopia, Uganda, Angola and Mozambique) were not included in the sample. Madagascar was excluded because data for the early sixties were not available. We used data published by the World Bank (World Tables 1976 and 1991). All data, except those on population, are from the national accounts.

Proxies were used for the change in the labour supply, DL, and in the capital stock, DK. In the absence of data on the former we used the growth of population. Gross domestic investment, with a one period lag, was used as a proxy of the change in the capital stock. Data on net investment would be preferable, but they are either not available or not reliable due to the poor quality of statistics on depreciation.

Two estimates of equation (8) were made. The first one is for the system as such. In the second the constants and the population variable were omitted, the former because they do not appear in the model of section 2.2 and population growth because it may be a poor proxy of labour supply and most population statistics are based on intra- and extra-populations.

2.4 ESTIMATION RESULTS

The estimation results of the full system (8) are given in table 2.1 and those for the system excluding the constants and population are given in table 2.2. The computation algorithm which was used, failed to yield estimation results for Zaire.

Consider first the results for the full system (8). In terms of statistical significance of the estimated coefficients, many of the results are rather poor. Given the remarks on the estimation of switching regression models in section 2.3, this is not unexpected. Happily, for a few countries, results are rather interesting.

Before starting a country by country analysis of the results, a general remark on the estimates of the population coefficient is in order. For all but five countries the estimated value of the population coefficient is smaller than its standard error. For three of these countries (Ivory Coast, Niger and Senegal) the estimated coefficient is negative. Again this is not quite unexpected given that population may be a poor proxy for labour inputs and that the data are probably not based on independent yearly observations.

Table 2.1 Regression results system (8) (a)

Country	Regime 1					Regime 2			Log L
	cst	DPOP	GDI	DX	o_1	cst	DM	o_2	
Burkina Faso	-21.9	0.02	0.64	-1.45	8.7	28.7	8.70	26.0	-120.57
	(9.6)	(0.06)	(0.17)	(1.21)	(3.7)	(7.2)	(3.74)	(9.6)	
Cameroon	-6.2	-0.03	0.51	0.32	62.1	308	4.340	75.8	-156.13
	(47.8)	(0.32)	(0.12)	(0.23)	(13.5)	(145)	(2.48)	(105.9)	
Ghana	-11.2	-0.22	0.21	-0.26	17.4	43.8	1.34	43.7	-129.96
	(73.0)	(0.11)	(0.48)	(0.34)	(5.2)	(29.1)	(0.83)	(11.8)	
Ivory Coast	121,4	0.10	0.30	0.19	11.4	115.8	0.88	101.5	-163.89
	(37.0)	(0.14)	(0.06)	(0.17)	(5.2)	(23.7)	(0.38)	(26.0)	
Kenya	-116	-20.57	0.86	0.32	3021	3920	0.40	3372	-273.42
	(12467)	(41.40)	(1.49)	(1.16)	(3161)	(959)	(0.70)	(785)	
Malawi	51.1	0.14	0.36	4.08	7.7	134.4	-0.03	95.2	-158.41
	(15.5)	(0.11)	(0.03)	(0.27)	(6.5)	(24.1)	(0.13)	(19.2)	
Mali	17.0	-0.10	0.73	5.35	5.9	24.5	-.094	18.6	-119.12
	(23.8)	(0.28)	(0.74)	(2.63)	(3.8)	(4.5)	(0.20)	(3.9)	
Niger	50.4	-0.13	0.27	0.26	4.5	17.7	0.31	53.4	-141.75
	(27.2)	(0.10)	(0.15)	(0.12)	(3.2)	(13.4)	(0.52)	(8.7)	

Nigeria	4510	6.49	-0.29	0.39	5110	2171	0.21	5877	-288.14
	(67821)	(50.54)	(0.92)	(0.63)	(5364)	(1948)	(0.15)	(1819)	
Rwanda	7.2	0.07	1.63	-1.01	0.65	3.7	0.91	7.2	-83.57
	(1.5)	(0.02)	(0.27)	(0.23)	(0.60)	(1.6)	(0.61)	(1.5)	
Senegal	-12.5	0.86	-0.41	1.12	21.0	70.1	-0.59	7.9	-144.85
	(20.6)	(0.35)	(0.27)	(0.23)	(7.7)	(23.2)	(0.72)	(21.5)	
Sudan	199	6.16	0.62	2.06	1884	474	2.86	1691	-255.28
	(26654)	(72.76)	(9.36)	(25.46)	(5836)	(630)	(1.91)	(60.)	
Tanzania	6267	-18.42	0.63	1.05	4024	5390	0.10	3898	-279.43
	(31014)	(95.16)	(2.84)	(5.07)	(10065)	(928)	(0.08)	(1093)	
Zambia	923	-4.37	0.73	-0.92	748	336	0.09	756	-231.96
	(618685)	(761.29)	(129.04)	(177.70)	(5494)	(176)	(0.10)	(191)	

(a) Standard error in parenthesis.

Table 2.2 Regression results system (8) without population of constants (a)

Country	Regime 1			Regime 2		Log L
	GDI	DX	o_1	DM	o_2	
Burkina Faso	0.46	-1.26	10.5	1.03	32.9	-131.78
	(0.11)	(1.70)	(6.6)	(0.72)	(7.2)	
Cameroon	0.59	0.48	37.3	5.15	298.5	-168.64
	(0.08)	(0.33)	(12.6)	(1.20)	(139.5)	
Ivory Coast	(b)					
Ghana	(c)					
Kenya	0.42	0.36	2929	1.40	4903	-285.79
	(0.33)	(0.78)	(4346)	(0.74)	(1152)	
Malawi	0.49	3.29	8.6	0.14	118.5	-170.75
	(0.29)	(0.33)	(12.4)	(0.17)	(29.0)	
Mali	0.90	2.50	21.5	-0.42	27.0	-134.65
	(0.84)	(14.65)	(43.6)	(0.41)	(5.8)	
Niger	0.63	0.35	12.6	0.73	59.6	-147.42
	(0.12)	(0.26)	(5.2)	(0.58)	(12.0)	

Nigeria	1.05	0.97	522	0.15	6178	-292.20
	(2.64)	(2.07)	(11052)	(0.11)	(1480)	
Rwanda	1.34	-1.25	1.86	1.46	7.94	-92.30
	(0.24)	(0.58)	(1.12)	(0.67)	(1.92)	
Senegal	0.51	0.72	18.2	0.45	66.2	-154.10
	(0.14)	(0.30)	(12.6)	(0.42)	(16.3)	
Sudan	(b)					
Tanzania	0.52	1.25	4663	0.19	6644	-295.30
	(0.89)	(3.30)	(11277)	(0.17)	(1539)	
Zambia	0.89	-1.24	747	0.08	818	-234.92
	(15.46)	(120.52)	(4305)	(0.08)	(128)	

(a) Standard error in parenthesis
(b) No results. Estimated variance matrix of estimates is singular
(c) No results. Algorithm could not locate likelihood function maximum.

The most reasonable results are obtained for Burkina Faso, Cameroon, Ivory Coast and Rwanda. For all four countries the coefficients of investment and of imports are significantly different from zero. The implicit marginal capital-output ratio (equal to the inverse of the investment coefficient) is in the range of 2 to 3, except for Rwanda, where it would be less than one. The point estimates of the import variable are higher than or close to one, the value put forward as a likely lower limit in section 2.2. (For Ivory Coast and Rwanda the import coefficient is not significantly different from one.) The values of the export coefficient estimates are less satisfactory; they are even negative for Burkina Faso and for Rwanda. The lack of correlation between GDP and export growth in low income countries is well-known from cross-section econometric analysis of the relation between export growth and GDP.[7] Our results, based on time series, confirm that observation.

Based on the regression results, the probability of import constrained growth in individual years can be calculated.[8] The results are shown in the figures in Appendix. According to the computations, in Cameroon there were no import shortages during the sixties and the seventies, but in 1982-84 and again in 1987-89 growth was import constrained. Both for Burkina Faso and for Rwanda, import shortages existed mainly in the seventies and the eighties, although in Rwanda the import constraint already dominated in individual years during the sixties. A quite different picture is obtained for Ivory Coast, where during the sixties and seventies periods with and without a binding import constraint alternated. But for this country also import constrained growth was the dominating regime during the eighties.

Less satisfactory results were obtained for Ghana and Sudan. The estimates of the regime 1 coefficients have high standard errors, especially for Sudan. For both countries the point estimate of the import coefficient is higher than, but not significantly different from one. The calculated probabilities of regime 2 are therefore less reliable. They are nevertheless also graphically represented in Appendix. For what they are worth they suggest that in Sudan growth was import constrained in every single year of the period under consideration. In Ghana before 1984 periods with and without a binding import constraint alternated. But in the years 1984-88 the probability of the existence of an import constraint was considerably less than 50%. This might reflect the impact of structural adjustment policies ad loans.

We now come to the countries for which the estimation results are poor. For Nigeria the point estimate of the import constraint coefficient is only 0.21 (with a standard error of 0.15), a result which is hardly credible. For four countries, Kenya, Niger, Tanzania and Zambia, the standard error of the import coefficient estimate is higher than or approximately equal to the point estimate. This would mean that in a year with an import constraint dominance, import growth had no statistically significant effect on GDP growth. This clearly does not make sense. For Nigeria the investment coefficient is negative. Note further the very poor estimation results for Tanzania and especially for Zambia. Finally for three countries, Mali, Malawi and Senegal, the estimated import coefficient is negative, and for Mali even significantly different from zero.

Summarising and generalising we have found weak to good evidence of import constrained growth in six of the fourteen countries for which we obtained results. In five of these countries import constrained years were more frequent during the seventies and especially the eighties than during the sixties.

Now consider the estimation results when the constants and the population variable are omitted from the regressions, which are presented in table 2.2. For three countries, Ivory Coast, Ghana and Sudan, the algorithm we used did not yield results. For Burkina Faso, Cameroon and Rwanda the results are more or less comparable to those of the full model. For regime 1, in the case of Burkina Faso and Rwanda the export coefficient remains negative. Moreover for Rwanda the investment coefficient is again higher than one implying a marginal capital-output ratio of less than one. In regime 2 the import coefficient is now appreciably lower for Burkina Faso and higher for Rwanda. For both countries the coefficients are within one standard error of one. For Cameroon the coefficient of the import variable is significantly higher than one. The computed probabilities suggest a somewhat higher frequency of import constrained years for Burkina Faso and for Cameroon, and a similar frequency for Rwanda.

For Kenya the regression results are more satisfactory when the constants and population are omitted. The import coefficient is higher than, though not significantly different from one. But the point estimate of the investment coefficient is only marginally higher than its standard error. In most years the computed probabilities of regime 2, shown in Appendix, are less than 50%; the exceptions are 1961, 1975, 1979 and 1981-82. This suggests that by and large economic growth in Kenya was not constrained by available imports.

For the remaining seven countries the estimated coefficient of the import variable is smaller or only marginally higher than the standard error and, with the exception of Niger, less than 0.5. For Mali, the estimate has again a negative sign. The estimated coefficients of the regime 1 variables, investment and export, or for at least one of them, are significantly different from zero in the case of Malawi (export), Niger (investment), and Senegal (investment and export). Estimates of the regime 1 coefficients for Mali and Nigeria have a relatively higher standard error. The least satisfactory results are again obtained for Tanzania and for Zambia.

Summarising the estimation results of our shifting regression model without the population variable and without constants, for three countries, Burkina Faso, Cameroon and Rwanda broadly similar results to those of the full model were obtained. For Kenya the estimation results improved; computed probabilities suggest that its growth was not import constrained. For the remaining countries results did not improve, either.

2.5 CONCLUSION

The purpose of this chapter was to test empirically whether limited imports have constrained growth in Sub-Saharan Africa. The test consisted of the estimation of a switching regression model for fifteen of the most populated SSA-countries. The results of the test were mixed. Only for a few countries the estimated coefficient of the import variable was greater than one, although this was expected on the basis of the model of section 2.2. For some other countries, the value of the coefficient was not significantly different from one. But there were also countries for which the estimated coefficient was not significantly different from zero or even negative. This of course is not reconcilable with the existence of an import constraint.

As for regime 1 only for three countries the estimate of the coefficient of population was significantly different from zero and for two of these it had a negative sign. For some countries the coefficients of the other regime 1 variables also had the 'wrong' sign or were not significantly different from zero.

We found good to weak evidence for the existence of an import constraint in six countries. For those countries the computed probability of an import constrained regime was higher during the seventies and especially the eighties than during the sixties. For one country, Kenya, the computed probabilities suggest that in most years imports did not constrain growth. For the remaining countries, the statistical results are too poor to allow any conclusion.

One may wonder why we did not find more evidence for the existence of import constrained growth in Sub-Saharan Africa. We can think of at least two explanations. First the model that was tested, is extremely simple. Ideally we should have a multiple equation model with a number of lags and with the possibility of different regimes. A multiple equation model would raise computational problems. We did not experiment with it. We did try out some lags for the right hand side variables without drastically different results. It would also be interesting to apply the model to more disaggregated data, e.g. to test whether intermediate imports have constrained industrial production. We did not do either this because the relevant data were not readily available.

The second explanation for the limited evidence on import constrained growth, is the gap between the data requirements of the switching regression model and the quality of the statistics for a number of SSA-countries. Estimating a switching regression model requires fairly long time series. The quality of at least some of the SSA-statistics is exceedingly low[9]. The quality of the data decreases the further one goes back in the past, as definitions and methods of data collection change over time. Econometric analysis in Sub-Saharan Africa should therefore preferably be directed towards those phenomena for which we have good quality data. This implies that data should be disaggregated and that we should preferably not use such heterogeneous aggregates as GDP or aggregate investment.

The results of the analysis suggest that raising the external purchasing power of some African countries may contribute to an increase of their growth rate. However we found no statistical evidence that this statement applies to the majority of the countries in the sample.

APPENDIX 2.1 : The Probability of Imports Constrained Growth in Individual Years.

Figure 2.1 Burkina Faso

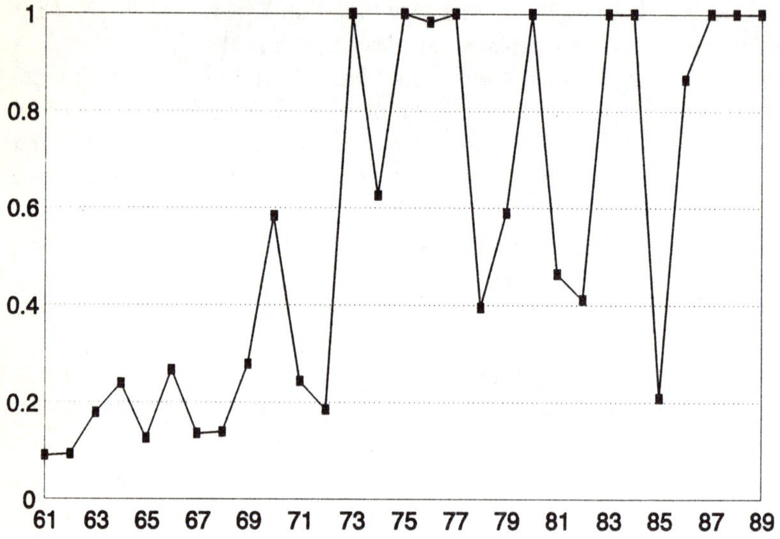

Figure 2.2 Cameroon

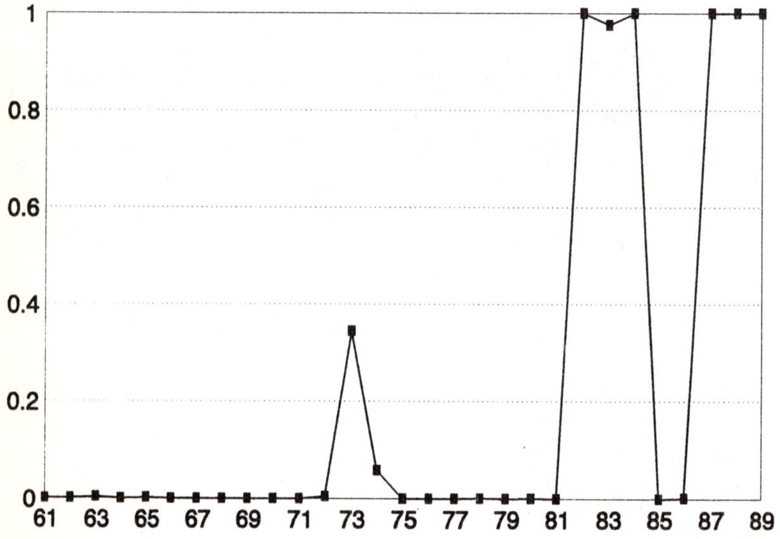

Figure 2.3 Côte d'Ivoire

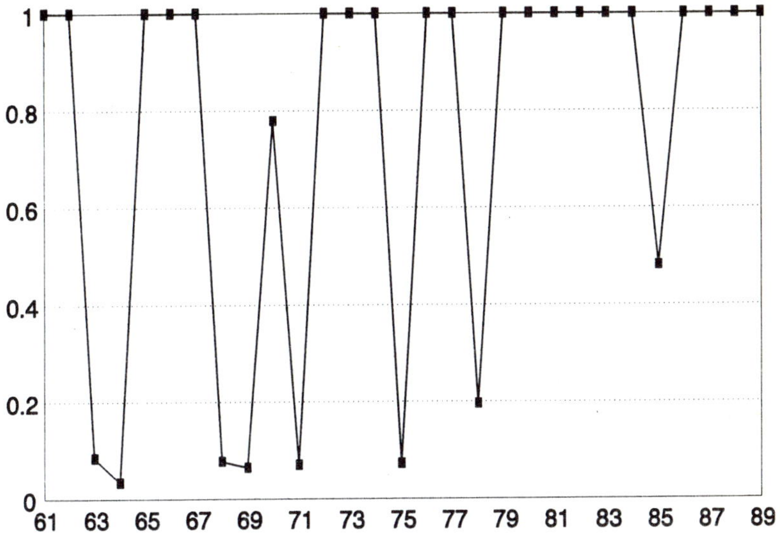

Figure 2.4 Rwanda

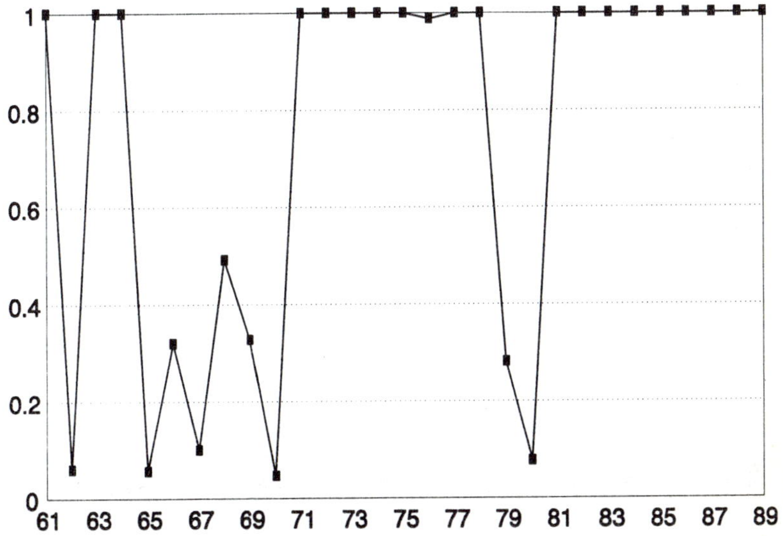

Figure 2.5 Ghana

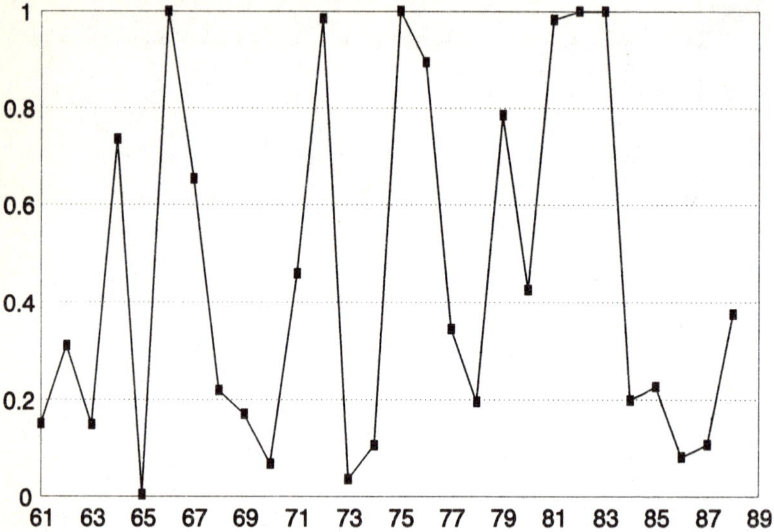

Figure 2.6 Sudan

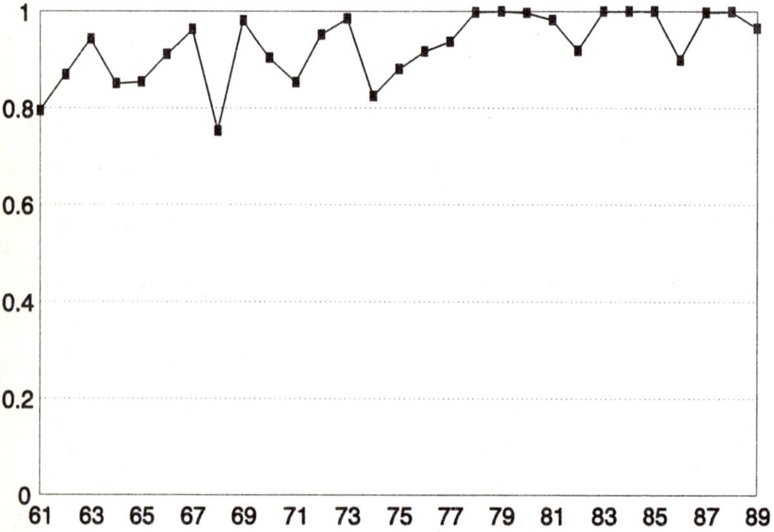

Figure 2.7 Kenya

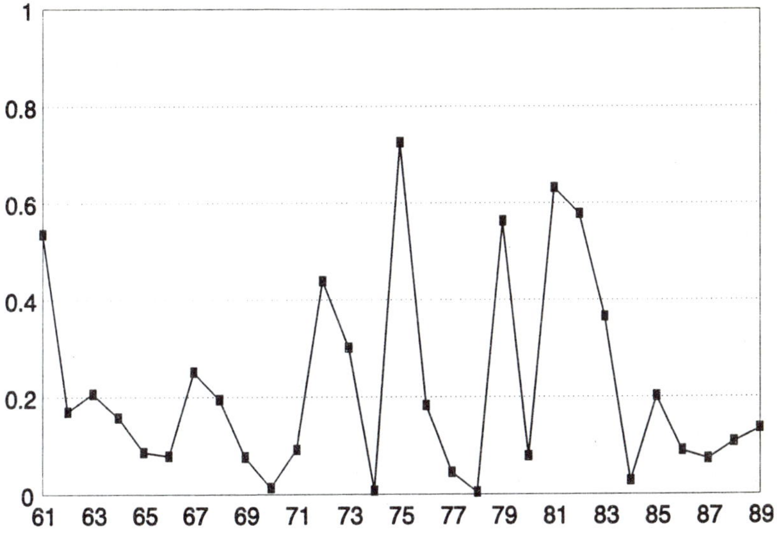

NOTES AND REFERENCES

1. This research was financed by a grant from the Belgian "Nationaal Fonds voor Wetenschappelijk Onderzoek" (NFWO). The authors thank A. Barten for comments.
2. The figures for 1960-73 and 1973-80 are from World Bank (1989). The figures for 1980-89 are based on World Bank, World Tables 1991. The global figures are of course an aggregate. Data for individual countries show a more heterogeneous reality. See e.g. World Bank and UNDP (1989).
3. An excellent reference for a balanced discussion of immediate and fundamental causes is Killick (1992). See also Pickett (1990) and Ravenhill (1986).
4. For recent econometric analyses of the impact of foreign exchange availability on imports see M.S. Khan and M.D. Knight (1988). R.E. Lopez and V. Thomas (1990), and S.H. Samiei (1990).
5. The impact of exports on GDP growth has been empirically analysed in numerous papers. They are usually based on cross-section evidence. A typical contribution in this tradition is G. Feder (1982).
6. For Ghana the number of observations is 28 as data for 1989 were not yet published.
7. See e.g. Feder (1982) and Helleiner (1986).

8. This probability, given the observed valuc of the dependent variable, is calculated as $f_2F_1/(f_1F_2+f_2F_1)$ were f_i is the value of the density function of regime i for the observed value of the dependent variable and F_i is equal to one minus the probability that under regime i the value of the dependent variable is less than or equal to its observed value.
9. For a discussion of the quality of trade statistics in SSA see Yeats (1990).

BIBLIOGRAPHY

COCKCROFT, L. (1990) *Africa's way, a journey from the past*, I.B. Tauris, London.

FEDER, G. (1982) 'On exports and economic growth', *Journal of Development Economics*, vol. 12, nos 1/2, pp. 59-73.

HELLEINER, G.K. (1986) 'Outward orientation, import instability and African economic growth: an empirical investigation', in Lall, S. and Stewart, F. (eds.) *Theory and reality in development*, MacMillan, Basingstoke.

HELLEINER, G.K. (1992) 'The IMF, the World Bank and Africa's adjustment and external debt problems: an unofficial view', *World Development*, vol. 20, no 6, pp. 779-792.

KHAN, M.S. and KNIGHT, M.D. (1988) 'Import compression and export performance in developing countries', *Review of Economics and Statistics*, vol. 70, no 2, pp. 315-321.

KILLICK, T. (1992) Explaining Africa's post-independence development experiences, Overseas Development Institute, London, Working paper no 60.

LÓPEZ, R.E. and THOMAS, V. (1990) 'Import dependency and structural adjustment in Sub-Saharan Africa', *World Bank Economic Review*, vol. 4, no 2, pp. 195-207.

MADDALA, G.S. (1986) 'Disequilibrium, self-selection, and switching models', ch. 28 in Z. Griliches and M.D. Intriligator (eds.), *Handbook of Econometrics*, vol. III, North-Holland, Amsterdam.

MADDALA, G.S. and NELSON, F.D. (1974) 'Maximum likelihood methods for models of markets in disequilibrium', *Econometrica*, vol. 42, no 6, pp. 1013-1030.

PICKETT, J. (1990) 'The low-income economies of Sub-Saharan Africa: problems and prospects', in J. Pickett and H. Singer (eds.), *Towards economic recovery in Sub-Saharan Africa, Essays in honour of Robert Gardiner*, Routledge, London and New York.

RAVENHILL, J. (1986) 'Africa's continuing crisis: the elusiveness of development', in J. Ravenhill (ed.), *Africa in economic crisis*, Columbia University Press, New York.

SAMIEI, S.H. (1990) 'Testing for balance of payment constraints: the case of the oil exporters', *Journal of Economic Studies*, vol. 17, no 5, pp. 3-18.

WORLD BANK (1989) *Sub-Saharan Africa. From crisis to sustainable growth, a long-term perspective study*, The World Bank, Washington, D.C.

WORLD BANK and UNDP (1989) *Africa's adjustment and growth in the 1980s*, The World Bank and UNDP.

YEATS, A.J. (1990) 'On the accuracy of economic observations: do Sub-Saharan trade statistics mean anything?', *World Bank Economic Review*, vol. 4, no 2, pp. 135-156.

3 The Effect of Prices on Trade during the First Twelve Years of the European Community

Herbert Glejser

3.1 INTRODUCTION

Unlike trade figures, *price* data have not been utilized to any large extent in the analyses carried out on the effects of the European Community (EC).

Yet, such data do exist. In this chapter, we shall use the survey of consumer prices carried out by the Statistical Office of the European Community in a particular city in each of the member countries between August and December 1958, the very months which preceded the first stage in the establishment of the Common Market treaty between the 'five' initial member-countries. (Luxembourg belongs to the Belgian Franc area and is not considered separately). The survey recorded 177 comparable items representing important components of goods consumed. The observations took place in all types of shops.

In October 1966 and April 1970, similar surveys were undertaken by the same Statistical Office. Effective prices paid by the consumer and not the catalogue prices were recorded.[1]

For trade data we used the 'OECD: Commodity Trade Statistics for 1966' and the 'EEC Statistical Office: Foreign Trade (Nimexe) 1970'.

Those data are used for two purposes:

1. An acid test of comparative cost theory where *pre-customs union* prices play the role of *pretrade* prices – a function which has been discussed previously by the author (Glejser, 1972).
2. An analysis of the effect of the variation of trade on the change in price disparities with the purpose of drawing, tentative conclusions about their supply or demand curves.

3.2 PRE-UNION PRICES AND TRADE

The following function has been chosen:

$$\left(\frac{X^P_{i,s}}{X^P_{j,s}}\right)_{1970} = \alpha_{i,j,s} \left(\frac{P^P_i}{P^P_j}\right)^{\beta_{i,j,s}}_{1958} * v \qquad p=1,2,\ldots,\pi \qquad [1]$$

where $X^P_{i,s}$ and $X^P_{j,s}$ stand for export of product p to country s, respectively from country i and j *in 1970* and X^P_i , X^P_j for the consumer price of the same good *in 1958* (Each variable is expressed in a common currency at existing exchange rates).

In the year 1970 the internal tariffs had been brought to zero since three years so that the long run effect could be assessed. Also 1970 was immune from the disruptions in the economy which characterized France especially in 1968 and 1969.

The parameter $\beta_{i,j,s}$ stands for the elasticity of substitution of good p from i to j on the market of s, whereas $\alpha_{i,j,s}$ is the ratio of export shares when prices i and j are equal in 1958. (We suppose those parameters to be equal over commodities. (see further).

Comparative advantages explained only part f the 1958 price disparities. Among the many other factors we find:

1. Various degrees of protectionism as among countries and goods;
2. Differences in the cost of services before and after production (distribution and transportation cost of services before and after production wage rates — of about 1 to 2 between Italy and West Germany — and the quality and modernity of the networks);
3. Differences in indirect — and to the same extent also direct taxes and subsidies;
4. The action of monopolies, cartels, etc. causing the price of some goods to exceed the free competition level in some countries;
5. Differences in the quality of the products. Although the investigators aimed at recording prices of *comparable* products, the question can be asked if Belgian and German chocolates are really comparable?;
6. Other errors of measurement — e.g. the varying effectiveness of bargaining at retail level in the various countries.
7. Last but not least, the fact that the prices are pre-union prices, rather than pretrade prices.

The first flaws in our data are of the type 'errors in variable' and would under reasonable assumptions pull towards zero the least squares estimates. The seventh flaw tends to push it away from zero: as the ratio of prices is too high, the elasticity ß is blown up.

8. There is an eighth assumption in our model, namely that the parameters α and ß are stable over commodities. That hypothesis has been verified several times — (see MacDougall, 1961; Kravis and Lipsey, 1971; Richardson, 1975) — although authors like Bhagwati (1964) expressed their 'astonishment' or even 'amazement' over such findings; but why should 'sauce for the goose not also be sauce for the gaunder'?

As the French Franc was clearly overvalued in 1958 (a devaluation occurred on December 31) whereas the Mark and the Guilder were undervalued — a revaluation took place in March 1961 — we use the late 1961 parities to convert all prices.

Only for 31 commodities did we find figures for trade as well as for prices — most of them in the sectors of clothing, food or consumer durables. We checked for a significant (at the 5% level) shift in α or in ß as between the two groups of durable and nondurable products. Out of 21 regressions, there never was a shift for ß, whereas it happened 5 times for log α. Four of these positive shifts occurred in the case of French clothing exports. Those shifts averages 0.915 which — ceteris paribus — meant an almost tenfold market share for France.

Our equations amount to a formidable test indeed as the trade and the figures for the pre-customs union are separated by a long period during which many structural changes took place: wages exploded in Italy and the Netherlands, while the French and Italian economies underwent a rapid industrialisation and showed high rates of growth. In addition the eight qualifications, which were mentioned above, also apply.

It is therefore most extraordinary to find out that in the 21 equations, the least-square estimator of ß differs significantly from zero in 6 cases at the 5% level and in 2 cases at the 1% level.

In no regression implying French exports is ß significant, with the right sign. (This holds true also in regressions where a dummy is used to account for the significant positive shift of French garment exports). That is why Table 3.1 only reports results where Germany, Italy, the Netherlands and Belgium appear as exporters: this time ß

Table 3.1 Most significant regression results (i.e. all of those excluding France as an exporter)*

Market	France		Germany		Italy		The Netherlands		Belgium	
Pair of exporters	log α	ß	log α	ß	log α	ß	log α	ß	log α	ß
Germany / Italy	0.15 (0.10)	-2.75^{ss} (0.89)	-	-	-	-	0.58^{ss} (0.14)	-0.83 (1.32)	0.55^{ss} (0.13)	-1.87 (1.21)
Germany / The Netherlands	0.73^{ss} (0.11)	-1.26 (1.10)	-	-	0.82^{ss} (0.10)	-1.64^{s} (0.93)	-	-	-	-
Germany / Belgium	0.33^{s} (0.15)	-3.69^{s} (2.18)	-	-	1.01^{ss} (0.09)	-2.37^{s} (1.27)	-	-	-	-
Italy / The Netherlands	0.51^{ss} (0.13)	-3.01^{ss} (1.04)	0.194 (0.141)	-2.04^{s} (1.16)	-	-	-	-	-	-
Italy / Belgium	0.16 (0.16)	-2.28 (1.69)	0.56^{ss} (0.13)	0.71 (1.34)	-	-	-	-	-	-

* The figures in parenthesis are the estimated standard errors of the coefficients. The symbols s and ss stand for significant, respectively at the 5% and 1% level (two-tailed test for log α and one-tailed test for ß).

has always a negative sign and is significant, at least at the 5% level, in 6 out of 11 cases.

In three cases ¦ ß ¦ is greater than 2.5: for the couples Germany-Italy, Germany-Belgium and Italy-the Netherlands each time on the French market. Also in three cases ¦ ß ¦ lies between 2 and 2.5: Italy-Belgium on the French market, Italy-the Netherlands on the German market and Germany-Belgium on the Italian market. There seems to be a tendency for demand elasticities to be higher on the large Latin markets, especially for France (where the lowest value of ¦ ß ¦ is 1.26).

As to α, it differs significantly from zero (at the 5% level) in 12 cases out of 21 and 8 out of 11 if we exclude French trade. It clearly reflects advantages in the field of:

1) supply capacity,
2) distance — both physical and psychic (e.g. similarity in he languages: Italy will be favoured vis-à-vis the Netherlands on the French market; or similarity of tastes, etc...).

As a matter of fact those factors strongly qualify comparative advantage as Germany seems to have an α ten times that of Belgium on the Italian market where the 'superiority' of Germany vis-à-vis the Netherlands almost reaches the same level. On the other hand, it appears to be close to and not significantly different from 1 in the case of Germany and Italy on the French market or of Italy and the Netherlands on the German market (*viz.* Table 3.1)[2].

Note also the strong similarity of log α in the case of Germany and Italy on the Dutch and on the Belgian markets as well as the similarity of Germany and the Netherlands on the French and Italian markets.

One should not lose sight of the fact, pointed out before, that the comparative price variable is blurred by considerable errors in the variable which most probably pull the coefficient ß towards zero. As measurement errors are smaller in export figures, a strong case can be made for estimating ß by regressing price on export ratios. To measure the extent of such a corrective device, one can calculate that the average of the six negative and significant ß's in Table 3.1 is -2.58. However, when we operate the permutation of the regressor and the regressand, the mean of the estimated ß falls to no less than -21 for the six cases considered! Some comparative cost theory!

A final way of testing the latter is to perform a sign test of the ß's; they are negative in 17 cases out of 21. Using the binominal test, it can be concluded that the zero hypothesis of independence of comparative exports and prices is rejected at the 1% significance level.

This means that despite the more recent rivalling theories which have been proposed to explain trade flows between developed countries, 'old' Ricardo still seems to be alive and kicking.

3.3 ON THE ELASTICITY OF THE SUPPLY CURVE

In the preceding section we examined the effect on trade in the pre-customs union prices. In this section we analyse how far exports from the cheapest source — for each good — to the most expensive countries in 1958, affect the price spread between the two in 1970 and 1958. We consider:

$$\Delta P^{P}_{i,s} = a + b\,\frac{\Delta X^{P}_{i,s}}{X^{P}_{i,s}} + c\left(\frac{\Delta X^{P}_{i,s}}{X^{P}_{i,s}}\right)^{2} + u,\ p = 1,2,\ldots,\pi, \qquad [2]$$

where

- $\Delta P_{i,s}$ stands for the *change* in the relative price discrepancy as between the expensive country i and the cheap country for product p over the period 1958-1970 (in percentage) i.e.:

$$\Delta P^{P}_{i,s} = 100\ .\left[\left(\frac{P^{P}_{i}}{P^{P}_{s}}\right)_{1970} - \left(\frac{P^{P}_{s}}{P^{P}_{s}}\right)_{1958}\right]$$

- and

$\frac{\Delta X^{P}_{i,s}}{X^{P}_{i,s}}$ is the relative change in the quantity of p exported from s to i as between *1970* and *1958* i.e.:

$$\frac{X^{s\to i}_{1970} - X^{s\to i}_{1958}}{X^{S\to I}_{1958}}$$

We expect the parameter a to be negative because of a spontaneous tendency of expensive local firms to reduce their price preventively for fear of and before any new inroad of imports.

The parameter b should be negative too as slowly increasing imports should mean lower prices with a positively sloped supply curve and a negatively sloped demand curve in the importing country.

Whether c is positive or negative depends on the change in supply and demand elasticity as imports grow: the supply curve should become more elastic as local production regresses and the least productive firms have been eliminated; on the other hand, the demand curve would become less elastic with increasing consumption as some satiation appears. We hypothesize the first effect to be stronger because prices remain relatively high in the importing nation — too early for real satiation. There are, of course, several weaknesses in our approach:

1) The assumption of identical parameters for all goods;
2) The neglect of income and production capacity increases in the *two* countries;
3) The ignorance of imports from other sources than the cheapest country;
4) The very low number of products observed: seven (contrary to the exercise described in section 2, we needed to have price and export figures for identical goods for two years instead of one).

Table 3.2 Relative price and export changes

Products	$100.\ \Delta P^P_{i,s}$ over 12 years	$\Delta X^P_{i,s} / X^P_{i,s}$ over 12 years	Countries i	Countries s
Chocolate	-63%	332.0	Italy	France
Marmalade	-29%	52.9	Italy	Netherlands
Beer	-12%	.3	Italy	France
Margarine	-11%	35.8	Germany	Netherlands
Toilet soap	-7%	10.5	Italy	Netherlands
Shoepolish	+2%	4.3	Germany	Netherlands
Detergent	+4%	3.5	Germany	Belgium

The change in price and in trade is impressive in two cases in Table 3.2 i.e. chocolate and marmalade; for the next three products — beer, margarine and toilet soap — the move towards price equalisation is moderate and trade growth is only important for the latter two. The disparity in the price of shoepolish and detergent increases (slightly) with a relative modest surge of trade. This curious evolution in relative prices is not exceptional: for 7 goods out of 36 the author found that disparities among member countries were higher in 1970 than in 1958 (Glejser, 1972).

The tremendous surge in trade shown in Table 3.2 for all products, except beer, indicates that income increases were only responsible for a small part of the growth in trade — at most, say, of a doubling.

Table 3.3 presents the estimates of a, b and c by a least square regression.

Table 3.3 Estimates of the parameters of equation (2).

a	b	c	R^2
-0.73	-0.45^{S}	$9.1.10^{-4}$	0.88
(4.46)	(-0.19)	$(5.7.10^{-4})$	-
-	-0.55^{SS}	$9.7.10^{-4S}$	-
-	(0.13)	$(3.9.10^{-4})$	-

As can be seen, a with the expected negative sign is small and insignificant. It was therefore dropped as shown in the second row of Table 3.2: b and c are hardly affected by the elimination of a, but their estimated standard errors declined notably and made them both significant, the first at the 1% and the second at the 5% level.

It is quite difficult to draw precise conclusions on supply and demand elasticities from these results. However if we hypothesize:

1) that the elasticity of demand is small compared to the elasticity of supply close to equilibrium;
2) that domestic supply is about ten times as large as imports (in reality, of course, imports come from many nations).

On the basis of these assumptions the elasticity of supply would be of the order of 20 in the neighbourhood of equilibrium.

In fact the supply elasticity does not vary much: even for $\frac{\Delta X}{X} = 10$ it only increases to 25 and it takes $\frac{\Delta X}{X} = 500$ — a surge never encountered here — to make it infinite.

These results also suggest that the welfare gain due to lower production costs in the EC have been much underestimated by surmising triangles probably 'thinner' than in reality.

3.4 CONCLUSION

A few strong conclusions emerge from the exercise which was carried out in this chapter: especially the relevance of Ricardo's comparative cost theory, also with regard to the trade between developed countries. Yet, other factors, some of them outside the scope of economics as such, also enter into play. For instance, Germany and the Netherlands lean towards each other and so do Belgium and France.

We also found that trade in the EC quite often tended to narrow down the price discrepancies between member countries because of a huge surge in trade in spite of the high supply elasticity in the importing country even during a boom period. We surmise that demand elasticity is on the very high side too. A value close to 10 does not seem exaggerated while supply elasticity would not be much below 20 in the neighbourhood of equilibrium. This indicates that elasticities which were much too low resulted in an underestimation of EC effects on welfare during the 1960s.

NOTES AND REFERENCES

1. This seems also to have been the case in the 1958 exercise although it is not stated explicitly.
2. See also the strong advantage of Italy over the Netherlands on the French markets and over Belgium on the German market - the latter results being somewhat unexpected. Observe finally the nonsignificant advantage of Germany over Belgium on the French market.

BIBLIOGRAPHY

BALASSA, B. (1963) 'An Empirical Demonstration of Classical Comparative Cost Theory', *Review of Economics and Statistics*, August.

BHAGWATI, J. (1964) 'The Pure Theory of International Trade: A Survey', *Economic Journal*, March, Section 1 (Theorems in Statics: the Pattern of Trade).

GLEJSER, H. (1967) 'An Explanation of Differences in Trade-Product Ratios among Countries', *Cahiers économiques de Bruxelles*, no 37, 1st quarter.

GLEJSER, H. (1972) 'Empirical Evidence on Comparative Cost Theory from the European Common Market Experience', *European Economic Review*.

HELLER, H.R. (1963) *International Trade, Theory and Empirical Evidence*, Prentice Hall. Inc., Englewood Cliffs, New Jersey.

INSEE (1968) *Annuaire Statistique de la France*, vol. 74, pp. 590, Paris.

KRAVIS, J.B. and R.E. LIPSEY (1971) *Price Competitiveness in World Trade*, Columbia University Press, New York.

MacDOUGALL, D. (1961) 'British and American Exports: a Study Suggested by the Theory of Comparative Cost', *Economic Journal*, December.

OECD (1966) *Commodity Trade Statistics*, series C.

Office Statistique de Communautés Européenes (1960) 'Revenus réels C.E.C.A. 1954-1958', *Statistiques sociales*, no 2, pp. 188.

Office Statistique de Communautés Européenes (1967) *General Statistical Bulletin*, no 4, pp. 14.

Office Statistique de Communautés Européenes (1970) *Foreign Trade, Analytic Tables* (Nimexe).

RICHARDSON, I.D. (1975) *On Improving the Estimate of the Export Elasticity of Substitution*, Mimeo, Department of Economics, University of Wisconsin, Madison, September.

STERN, R. (1962) 'British and American Productivity and Comparative Costs in International Trade', *Oxford Economic Papers*, October.

4 Contingent Protection and International Trade: An Analysis of the Antidumping Policy of the European Union

P.K. Mathew Tharakan
and Birgit Kerstens

4.1 INTRODUCTION

During the post-World War II years, the GATT has had remarkable success in securing widespread reduction of tariff protection. The recently concluded Uruguay Round also made some progress in reaching agreement on gradually dismantling some kinds of non-tariff barriers (NTBs). But at the same time, there appears to be an increasing tendency on the part of some of the leading members of the WTO to use certain forms of contingent protection permitted by the rules of the GATT (WTO)[1].

The main types of contingent protection are: antidumping (AD) measures, countervailing duties (CVD) and escape clause provisions. These measures were meant by the GATT for corrective purposes and not as tools of commercial policy. Yet, the sharp increase in the number of petitions filed under such provisions and the lack of transparency of the related rules and decisions raise the doubt whether the mechanism is being diverted for protectionist purposes.

In this chapter we analyse the antidumping policy of the European Union (EU)[2].The ambiguities contained in AD rules in general, and of those of the EU in particular, are analysed in section 4.2. In section 4.3 we briefly review some of the available evidence concerning the dumping and injury decisions of the EU. The problem related to the estimation of the injury margin which is the most glaring weakness of EU's AD practice, is analysed in depth in section 4.4. Alternative estimates of injury for a large sample of cases are carried out. The results obtained are used in further empirical analysis. The conclusions are summed up in section 4.5.

4.2 THE LOOPHOLES

The ambiguities contained in the antidumping regulations in general and those which are specific to the EU in particular, are well-known (see Bellis (1990), Rycken (1991), Vermulst (1987)) and need no detailed repetition here. The following conditions have to be met before antidumping duties can be imposed in the European Union:

a) dumping has taken place;
b) dumping has caused or is threatening to cause material injury to the like-product industry of the European Union; and
c) it is in the Community's interest to impose an antidumping duty.

The determination of dumping involves four standard steps: the determination of 'normal value', the determination of export price, the adjustments necessary to assure comparability, and the calculation of the dumping margin as the difference between the two. The usual method of the determination of normal value is by reference to the price paid or payable on the domestic market of the country of origin or export. But since this approach may not be always operational, 'normal value of the like product' will have to be often established on the basis of the export sales of third countries or of 'constructed value'. If the latter option is taken, then allowance will have to be made for 'reasonable' overheads and profits. Similarly, under certain circumstances (e.g. the likely existence of a compensatory arrangement between the exporter and the importer), the Commission will choose to 'construct' the export price, making allowance for all costs incurred between importation and resale, including all duties and taxes, in addition to a 'reasonable' profit margin. In both cases, the procedure creates the risk of artificial dumping findings if overestimation of profit margins or overhead costs is made.

The overestimation of the profit margins and overhead costs is not the only way in which the antidumping rules can be manipulated for protectionist purposes. A bigger problem comes from the fully-allocated cost method often used and the stipulation, according to Article 2(4b) of regulation (EEC) No. 2423/88, which states that costs which are not covered in a reasonable way within the period of one year under investigation cannot be considered as in the normal course of business. There is no economic rationale why firms should follow the fully-allocated cost approach in their pricing policies. Particularly firms in the industries characterizedby heavy research and development expenditures and steep learning curves could find themselves highly vulnerable. A product learning curve is the plot of yield versus time. As optimal production conditions are obtained in a plant, there can be very big unit price declines. Since the early phases of production thus yield not only output, but also cost-reducing experience, firms might tend to 'forward price', i.e. price below current cost. Such a practice would clearly put firms in industries with steep learning curves in considerable risk of affirmative dumping findings, although the post-Uruguay Round changes in the regulations have alleviated this problem somewhat.

Another difficulty arises from the WTO permitted restrictive approach in determining dumping in the case of imports from centrally planned economies (CPEs). In such cases, normal value is determined on the basis of one of the following criteria: (a) the price at which the like product of a market economy third country is actually sold for consumption on the domestic market or to other countries; (b) the constructed value of the like product in a market economy third country or, (c) the price actually paid or payable in the EU for like product, duly adjusted, if necessary. All three of the above have a built-in affirmative finding bias.

Since the very fact that an AD procedure was initiated usually implies that the import price is less than the price at which the like product is sold in the EU, the use of the criterion (c) will almost certainly lead to a dumping finding. Criteria (a) and (b) are also disadvantageous to the defendants because the crucial element is the choice of the market economy 'analogue country' and the complainants are the ones who invariably propose the analogue country to be selected. The price of a like product in a market economy analogue country can be higher due to various reasons such as higher levels of production costs, high levels of protection, important degree of concentration, etc.

European Union's antidumping regulations and practice contain certain particularities as far as the injury determination is concerned (see Tharakan (1993)). The strict confidentiality rule which the EU follows means that the investigating authorities are the only ones with access to the complete file concerning the case. This can be particularly disadvantageous to the defendants in defending against claims of injury.

The non-confidential summaries of confidential information made available by the Commission are apparently of little use to the defendants. Experts have pointed out that such a situation could create an increased propensity to affirmative findings, particularly in the injury determination.

An equally important problem is the determination of the injury margin. The two preferred methods of the EU authorities for this purpose seem to be 'price undercutting' and 'price underselling' (see Vermulst and Waer (1991)). The former consists of the comparison of adjusted, weighted average resale prices of foreign producers with the prices of similar models/products of EU producers. The amount obtained by such a comparison is the 'price undercutting per unit'. But if the investigators are of the opinion that the prices of the EU producers have been depressed because of dumping, they will construct 'target prices' consisting of the full costs of the EU producers and a 'reasonable' or 'target' rate of profit. This 'target price' will be then compared with the adjusted price of comparable foreign models in order to obtain the per unit amount of 'price underselling'. Both methods have serious weaknesses which have been mentioned in some detail elsewhere (Tharakan (1993)). The most fundamental problem is that neither method tells us what the margin of injury would have been if there were no dumping.

The 'community interest clause' contained in the EU regulations does in fact provide the possibility for a more balanced implementation of the antidumping policy. It empowers the EU to consider, even in cases where dumping and injury were proved, whether the gains to the consumers from the lower prices more than outweigh the losses suffered by the producers. Unfortunately the conditions related to dumping and to injury have apparently had a greater influence than community interest clause in the EU decisions. As Messerlin ((1991), pp. 61-62) points out, before 1982, the Commission showed a tendency to take into account this condition mainly when the product involved was a raw material which was required as an input by the European Union producers and such industrial users mounted a major lobbying effort against the imposition of antidumping duties. Hoekman (1995) argues that one of the reasons why the community interest clause has not been effective is that no guidance is usually given to investigators how to weigh the injury to producers against the injury to consumers. The parties who might be negatively affected should also have the opportunity and the legal standing to present their arguments to the investigators. In this context it is interesting to note that the EU's community interest clause was strengthened in 1994 by an amendment to the antidumping legislation which gave legal standing to the consumers.

4.3 SOME PRELIMINARY EVIDENCE

The preceding analysis has clearly shown that there are certain ambiguities and loopholes in the antidumping regulations which can be made use of for protectionist purposes. Whether this has happened or not, is of course an empirical question. In this section we shall briefly review some of the empirical evidence available on this question with reference to the European Union.

Empirical work on contingent protection has made some progress in recent years. Useful information has become available from country studies and econometric work[3].The country studies have covered the evidence related to the leading users of the antidumping mechanism, namely Australia, Canada, EU and USA In addition, econometric work on the determinants of contingent protection, particularly in relation to USA and EU, has made some headway.

The econometric analysis of the determinants of the contingent protection in the EU (Schuknecht (1992), Tharakan and Waelbroeck (1994)) has been carried out within the framework of the model of administered protection developed by Finger, Hall and Nelson (FHN) (1982). Essential to the FHN model is the distinction between the political and technical tracks of protection. In the former, political influences are brought to bear on individual trade disputes. Technical track decisions such as AD/CVD determinations are made administratively. The technical track helps the government to shift the blame by pointing out to the losing side that no other decision was possible according to the rules. The FHN model includes both political and technical variables in the regressions concerning dumping and injury determinants but expects that the technical variables will perform better in the former, while the political variables will predominate in the latter.

In the logit regression analysis that was carried out in Tharakan and Waelbroeck (1994), a dichotomous dependent variable was used to represent the antidumping cases in which an affirmative finding was made, and those on which the complaint was rejected. A similar 1, 0 specification of the dependent variable was used in the injury/no injury decisions. The regressions covered every case decided during the period 1980-1987 by the EU. The political track variables included those representing international political influences and domestic political influences. The group of technical track variables consisted of comparative cost indicators designed to identify any protective bias in the AD/CVD mechanism in favour of those domestic produces who suffer from a comparative disadvantage in capital intensive industries. Other technical variables included a dummy representing the cases involving firms from centrally planned economies which are apparently vulnerable, as explained earlier, to affirmative dumping decisions because of some of the technical criteria codified in the dumping regulations.

The regression results showed some interesting patterns. As far as the dumping decisions were concerned, the political variables did not, with one exception, yield any significant results. Neither the danger of retaliation by the defendants' country, nor the lobbying capacity of the complainant industry, case size or employment considerations seem to significantly affect the EU's dumping decisions. But unlike the political track variables, a number of technical track variables performed well in the dumping regressions. Particularly important was the role of comparative costs variables such as physical capital intensity and average wages. The dumping decisions tend to be in favour of the European industries with high labour intensity. There seems to be also a tendency to protect industries with high wages and salaries. The results also showed that the firms from the centrally planned economies are in fact vulnerable to affirmative dumping decisions.

Interestingly, the results for the injury regressions showed a different pattern. A number of political track variables, particularly domestic political influences, yielded significant results. The most interesting example is industry concentration which was used as a proxy for lobbying potential. It was positively and very significantly correlated with affirmative injury decisions. Similarly, industries with high value added are also apparently influential in obtaining antidumping protection in their favour. In contrast, the technical track variables performed poorly in the injury regressions.

Our descriptive analysis of the antidumping regulations and practice of the EU carried out in section 4.2 showed that they are characterized by a number of ambiguities which could lend themselves to protectionist uses. It was further seen in that section that such potential for misuses of the antidumping rules are greater in the case of injury determinations. The results of the econometric analysis reviewed in the present section confirm that opinion. While political and technical variables are apparently pertinent in dumping and injury determinations, the former set of variables are more important in injury decisions than in dumping decisions. We shall now proceed to investigate in more depth the pattern of injury decisions by the EU.

4.4 THE QUESTION OF INJURY

4.4.1 An alternative approach: The CADIC model

As our analysis in section 4.3 makes clear, one of the major problems of the injury determination process used in the EU is that it could impute to 'dumping', injury that might have been caused by other factors. Ideally, the exercise should consist of disentangling the various causes of injury and ascribing to dumping that part of such injury it might have caused. In order to assess the effect of dumping on the like product industry of the importing industry, one has to ascertain how the condition of that industry would differ from its current state, had dumping not occurred, and then carry out a comparison with the factual world to determine the extent to which dumped products change prices and quantities. Unfortunately this kind of counterfactual analysis is not carried out by the EU in its injury investigations. But such an alternative method of injury investigation is contained in the Comparative Analysis of the Domestic Industry Condition (CADIC) model developed by Boltuck (1991) and which is being increasingly used by the parties concerned, in the United States International Trade Commission (ITC) injury investigations.

The theoretical background of the CADIC model, the underlying assumptions and the different steps contained in it have been elaborated elsewhere (see Boltuck (1991), Vandenbussche (1996)) and will not be explained here. Basically, the analysis proceeds in 3 steps. First, the dumping margin and certain other relevant data are used to calculate the price effect on the imports concerned, in the absence of dumping. Then the change in the price of such imports ('due to dumping') is used to estimate the change in demand for the domestic product. The final step makes use of the demand shift to calculate the price and quantity effects on the domestic like product due to dumping. The method is applicable whether the 'dumped' imports and the domestic like product are perfect or imperfect substitutes.

An important element in carrying out the exercise contained in the first step mentioned above, is to calculate the price (P_i) which the defendant would have charged if his market and the market of the complainant were integrated and if he were forced to charge a single price for both markets (i.e. no dumping takes place). In the CADIC model, P_i is defined as follows in terms of the basic parameters:

$$P_i = C / 1 \{ 1 + 1 [a \times N_h + (1 - a) \times [N_u + (N_{ud} \times N_{du}) / (E_d - N_d)] \} \quad [1]$$

where C = average (marginal) cost of production

a = the market share of the exporter (defendant) in the new, integrated market without dumping,

N_h = the own-price elasticity of demand in the defendant's market for the (dumped) products,

N_u = the own-price elasticity of demand in the complainant's market for the dumped product,

N_{du} = the cost-price elasticity of demand for the complainants industry's like product with respect to the price of the dumped products,

N_{ud} = the cost-price elasticity of demand for the dumped product with respect to the price of the complainant's like product,

E_d = elasticity of supply of the like-product,

and

N_d = elasticity of demand for the complainant's like-product.

In a counterfactual world of an integrated market, and in the absence of dumping, equation [1] defines the necessary condition for profit maximization by the exporter (defendant).

P_i has to be compared with the price (P_u) which the exporter would have charged in order to maximize his profits if dumping (price discrimination between markets) were possible. In terms of the basic parameters, the CADIC model defines P_u as follows:

$$P_u = C / \{ 1 + 1 / [N_u + (N_{ud} \times N_{du}) / (E_d - N_d)] \} \quad [2]$$

Once P_u and P_i are calculated, the percentage change in the price of the dumped import due to dumping can be calculated as,

$$\delta \ln P_u = (P_u - P_i) / P_i \quad [3]$$

P_u is generally negative, as $P_u < P_i$.

When $\delta \ln P_u$ has been estimated, the change in the complainant industry's like-product ($\delta \ln P_d$), which represents the margin of injury caused by dumping is calculated as follows:

$$\delta \ln P_d = (\delta \ln P_d / \delta \ln P_u) \times \delta \ln P_u \qquad [4]$$

There are a number of assumptions underlying this approach to the estimation of the injury caused to the domestic like product industry by dumping (see Boltuck (1991), Vandenbussche (1996)). Price dumping, as distinct from predatory pricing is assumed. Again, the import competing domestic industry is supposed to be a price-taker. Finally the dumping margins estimated by the authorities are assumed to be correct. All these assumptions can be criticised, but the invalidation of any of them is not likely to cause a fatal flaw to the exercise. While the possibility of predatory dumping cannot be excluded, its occurrence is unlikely. Domestic industry can of course be oligopolistic, but the very fact that there are dumping complaints suggests that it is not entirely free to set prices. While the dumping margins estimated by the authorities might be inflated, it only strengthens the basic thrust of the counterfactual experiment if the results, nevertheless show overestimation of injury.

The model is implemented in spreadsheet form as CADIC Lotus Template System. It is done by the user introducing as inputs the necessary parameter values. It is possible to operate the template by either specifying the full set of parameters, or one of several sub-sets of more commonly available parameters. When the latter option is taken, the theoretical framework of the model is applied automatically by the programme to generate consistent estimates of the necessary additional parameters. These are then used to calculate the reductions in price (and volume) of the like-product. We have taken this option and the subsets of parameters we introduced consisted of:

V_u = the market share of the dumped imports in the EU after the dumping,

V_d = the market share of the EU like product in the EU after the dumping,

a' = the share of the defendant's local sales in its combined export and local foreign sales,

E_f = supply elasticity of the fairly traded imports in the EU,

E_d = supply elasticity of the EU like product in the EU,
N_d = demand elasticity of the EU like product in the EU,
M = the dumping margin.

While the first two variables and the dumping margin are relatively easy to obtain, the determination of the value of the other parameters runs into various sorts of problems. The supply and demand elasticities, and parameter a' where not available, had to be specified on the basis of 'reasonable' assumptions. Fortunately, the sensitivity of small parameter changes to the final result do not appear to be important (see Bub 1996)

The use of parameter a' requires a brief clarification. As shown in equation [1], the parameter P_i is determined by, among other variables, the parameter 'a' which represents the market share of the exporter (defendant) in the counterfactual, integrated market without dumping. Specifically,

$$a = D_h / (D_h + D_u) \qquad [5]$$

where D_h = demand for the defendant's product, and D_u= the demand for the dumped product in the complainant's market.

But the parameter a' is in turn, interactive with P_i and when calculated in terms of non-dumping prices, has to be written as:

$$a = D_h (P_i) / [D_h (P_i) + D_u (P_i)] \qquad [6]$$

Consequently 'a' is not observable in a world where dumping has occurred. What is observable is a' which is the market share of the exporter after dumping has occurred. In operating the CADIC template, the user introduces this parameter value in the spreadsheet. The template assumes constant elasticity demand functions for D_h and D_u and then solves interactively for values P_i and a (see Boltuck (1991) pp. 117-118 and 123-124).

Figure 4.1 Injury margins estimated by the European Union (IMEU)

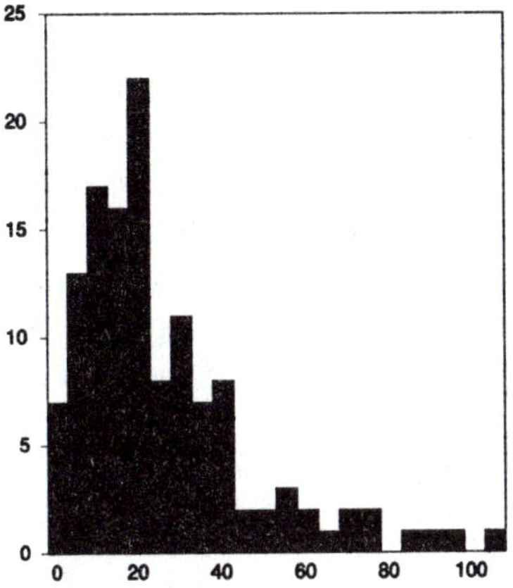

Senes/IMEU	
Sample 1 129	
Observations 127	
Mean	27.37622
Median	22.00000
Maximum	105.3000
Minimum	0.000000
Std. Dev.	20.63727
Skewness	1.539449
Kurtosis	5.433501
Jarque-Bera	81.49982
Probability	0.000000

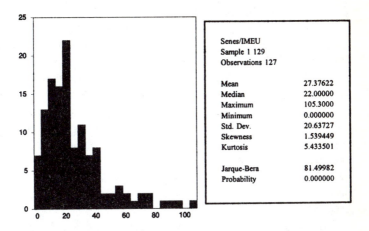

Figure 4.2 Alternative injury margins simulated by the CADIC Model

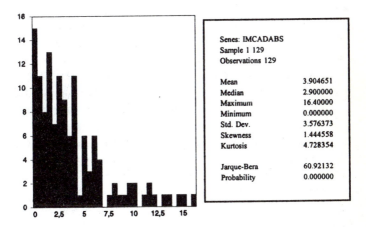

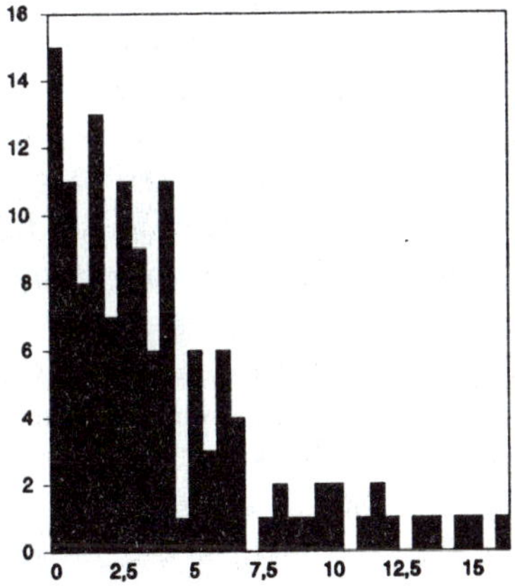

Senes: IMCADABS	
Sample 1 129	
Observations 129	
Mean	3.904651
Median	2.900000
Maximum	16.40000
Minimum	0.000000
Std. Dev.	3.576373
Skewness	1.444558
Kurtosis	4.728354
Jarque-Bera	60.92132
Probability	0.000000

4.4.2 Analysis of injury margins

We have used the CADIC model to simulate alternative injury decisions for 200 EU antidumping cases covering the period 1980-1994. Out of this sample, we have retained for further analysis 129 observations for which we could find matching variables in the econometric analysis carried out in the ensuing subsection. Hence the present analysis is restricted to the sample of 129 injury decisions.

Figure 4.1 shows the frequency distribution of the injury margin calculated by the EU in the above mentioned sample. It shows that in a significant number of cases the estimated injury margin hovered between about 10 and 25 per cent. There are much higher injury estimates of course with the highest estimated margin in the present sample being 205.3 per cent. The mean of the injury margins is 27.37 per cent.

These figures contrast sharply with the picture emerging from figure 4.2 in which the frequency distribution of the alternative injury margins simulated by the use of the CADIC model is presented. The mean of the alternative injury margins in this case is much lower at 3.9. The highest injury margin obtained is only 16.4. The inevitable inference that emerges from this contrast is that the mechanism used by the EU leads to systematic overestimation of the margin of injury.

We have calculated the difference between the injury margins estimated by the EU and those obtained by the CADIC simulation, for each one of the cases included in the sample. The difference obtained between the two is in fact a sort of 'unfairness index'. The higher the difference between the two, the greater is the penalization of the defendant through the injury estimation mechanism used by the EU.

In table 4.1 we have listed the ten cases in which the highest difference between the EU estimates and the CADIC estimates occur. The most striking fact is that Japan and the centrally planned economies together account for practically all the cases listed, with the case pertaining to the USA and Yugoslavia being the only exceptions. In fact Japanese firms were the defendants in 4 out of the 10 cases mentioned in table 4.1.

Table 4.1 Cases with the highest differences in injury estimates

Product	Country	Difference in injury estimates (% points)
Espadrilles	China	95.8
TV Cameras	Japan	84.4
EPROMs	Japan	81.0
Urea	Yugoslavia	69.9
Linear tungsten halogen lamps	Japan	69
Large aluminium electrolyte capacitors	Japan	69
Paint brushes	China	55.2
Copper sulphate	Bulgaria	53.7
Copper sulphate	USSR	51.8
Ethanolamine	USA	51.2

Source: Own calculations.

The products involved in the cases shown in table 4.1 have varied characteristics. Some of them are clearly high technology products while others are not. The vulnerability of the Japanese firms to dumping related decisions of EU in recent years has been noted by some authors (Belderbos (1994), Tharakan (1991)). One of the reasons for the inflated injury margins characterizing the Japanese cases could be that the products involved are often high technology products. Forward pricing practices combined with the EU's injury determination method (described in section 4.2) would yield inflated margins. In four out of the remaining six cases reported in table 4.1, the defendants were from (then) centrally planned economies. But of course general conclusions about the relationship between injury margin differences and the industry, and country characteristics of the cases involved would require a more comprehensive analysis to which we turn now.

4.4.3 An econometric exercise

The analysis presented in sections 4.2 and 4.3 indicate some variables which might explain the difference between the injury margins obtained through the method used by the EU and the more appropriate counterfactual estimates obtained through the CADIC model. Political economy factors, particularly the capacity to exert pressure seem to influence injury decisions (Tharakan and Waelbroeck (1994), Schuknecht (1992)). EU's injury margin estimation procedure can lead to biased results in the case of high technology industries. Further, centrally planned economies and more recently Japan, seem to be often the victims of some harsh decisions. These considerations suggest that the differences in the injury estimates can be tested through the following regression equation:

$$DIFF_i = f(CON_i, HITEC_i, CPE, JAPAN)$$

where

$DIFF_i$ = the difference between the injury estimate for industry i obtained by the EU and those obtained through the use of the CADIC model

CON_i = a dichotomous variable which identifies the cases initiated by associations of industries in which 25 % or more of the output is produced by five firms

$HITEC_i$ = a dichotomous variable in which the high technology industries take the value of 1 and others zero

CPE = a dummy variable which takes the value of 1 in all cases where the defendant is from a centrally planned economy

JAPAN = a dummy variable identifying the cases in which the defendants are Japanese firms

The above specification amounts to a single equation model of the type usually used in the analysis of trade policy decisions. No problem of simultaneity arises with respect to the equation. No forgotten feedback comes to mind where one of the independent variables would be influenced to a meaningful extent by the dependent variable. There are no a priori indications as to what the most suitable functional form should be. We have chosen to use a simple OLS functional form for the regression. A positive correlation between the dependent variable would indicate that the extent of the unfairness resulting from the injury determination process increases in the cases having the characteristics identified by the explanatory variables.

The results of the regressions are reported in table 4.2.

Table 4.2 Regression results

Variable	Coefficient	Std. Error	T-Statistic
C	15.09933	2.858009	5.283165
CON_i	1.178168	3.487359	0.337839
$HITEC_i$	13.07812	4.725192	2.767744
CPE	9.581886	3.454032	2.774117
JAPAN	11.58536	4.879937	2.374079
R-squared	0.163487		

The concentration coefficient has yielded a positive sign, but it is not significant at any of the acceptable levels. As would be recalled, earlier regression results (reviewed in section 4.3) had confirmed that complainant industries having a high degree of concentration were getting their way in injury decisions. The present results suggest that the potential lobbying effect represented by the degree of concentration of the complainant industry is not significantly influencing the extent of unfairness in the estimation of the injury margins. In other words, while the injury findings might be the result of effective lobbying by the complainants, the inflated injury margins are not the direct result of such lobbying.

The results of the $HITEC_i$ variable shows that firms in high technology industries tend to become victims of unfairly high injury margin estimates. In the analysis in section 4.2 we have clearly seen that the 'price undercutting' and 'price underselling' methods used by the EU in estimating the injury margins have the potential for overestimating the injury in the case of industries with high research and development expenditures. The above results confirm this conjecture.

The regression results obtained for the variables CPE and JAPAN show that the defendants from the centrally planned economies and Japan tend to be discriminated against in the estimation of injury margins. This confirms the general impression obtained from the analysis of the AD procedure of the EU and the outcome of our counterfactual exercise. In the case of the firms from the centrally planned economies, the overestimation of the injury margin is probably the result of the bias built into the mechanism itself. In the case of the Japanese firms, it could be partly due to commercial policy factors and partly because, as suggested earlier, Japanese firms tend to export mainly high technology products. Note that the simple correlation coefficient between HITEC and JAPAN at 0.3678 was the highest in the correlation matrix. The R^2 at 0.16 is low, as could be expected for a cross section regression, and suggests that we have not identified all the determinants of the inflated injury estimates.

4.5 CONCLUSIONS

The antidumping provisions are being increasingly used by some of the important trading nations. But such provisions contain a number of ambiguities which make it possible to divert this corrective mechanism for protectionist purposes. The European Union's AD regulations are no exception to this rule.

An analysis of the EU's antidumping regulations and practices shows that in addition to some of the loopholes contained in the dumping determination procedure, there are important problems connected with the injury assessment. Available econometric evidence from earlier studies indicate that the injury determination is particularly prone to the influence of political economy variables such as lobbying efforts.

In this paper we have extended the analysis of the injury determination of the EU. For this purpose we have first calculated alternative injury estimated using the counterfactual CADIC model. Our results show that in the vast majority of cases the EU has overestimated the injury margin.

We have then proceeded to econometrically test the variables which can explain the extent of the difference between the EU's injury estimates and those obtained by CADIC simulations. Our results indicate that defendants exporting certain kinds of products and belonging to certain countries tend to be penalized in the injury estimations. For example, firms exporting high technology intensive products are usually subjected to artificially inflated injury margins. Defendants from centrally planned economies and Japan also suffer from such a drawback.

Much has been written about the need to improve the antidumping rules and practices of the WTO members. Our preliminary results reported in this study indicate that there is an important problem with the injury estimation procedure used by the EU which unfairly penalizes certain exporters. Use of more appropriate methods, particularly those based on counterfactual analysis, would be a step in the right direction.

DATA SOURCES

The parameter values necessary for the CADIC simulation were obtained as follows: M, V_d and V_u were obtained from various issues of the Official Journal of the European Communities. The parameters a', E_d and N_d are based on own estimates, where possible in consultation with industry sources. $DIFF_i$ is the difference between the EU injury margin and the CADIC simulations. CON_i is built on the basis of the information collected from the following sources: whether the complainant is a professional association or not was ascertained from the relevant issue of the EC Official Journal; whether in the industry (NACE three digit level) level concerned, five firms accounted for at least 25 per cent of the output in the EU was ascertained from the Commission of the European Communities (1989, p. 41). $HITEC_i$ is based on the information available from EUROSTAT (1989) which lists, at SITC 5 digit level, the products which are considered as technology intensive. The correspondence between SITC 5 digit and CN 8 digit was made on the basis of the information given in the E.C. Official Journal, serie L 368, 29.12.1986. CPE and JAPAN are dummies identifying the AD cases involving defendants from the centrally planned economies and Japan respectively.

NOTES AND REFERENCES

1. During the period from July 1985 to June 1992, all countries together filed 1040 antidumping cases (Finger and Fung [1994])
2. During the period for which data are analysed in this study, the present day European Union was of course known as the European Communities (EC). In some particular cases (e.g. while referring to specific case documents) we shall revert to the old usage. Note also that we confine the empirical part of our analysis to AD cases, since it is by far the most important component of contingent protection.
3. See Finger (1993) for a collection of country studies, and Tharakan (1995) for an overview of econometric evidence.

BIBLIOGRAPHY

BELDERBOS, R. (1994), *Strategic Trade Policy and Multinational Enterprises: Essays in Trade and Investment by Japanese Electronics Firms*, Rotterdam, Tinbergen Institute Research Series.

BELLIS, J.F. (1990), 'The EEC Antidumping System', in J.H.Jackson and E.A. Vermulst (eds.), *Antidumping Law and practice: A Comparative Study*, Harvester Wheatsheaf, New York, pp. 41-97.

BUB, L. (1996), *Dumping en schade: Analyse van het Antidumpingbeleid van de Europese Unie (dumping and injury: analysis of the antidumping policy of the European Union)*, unpublished thesis, Antwerpen, 143 p.

EUROSTAT (1989), Statistical Analysis of Extra-EUR12 Trade in Hi-tech Products, Luxembourg.

FINGER, J.M. (1993) (ed.), *Antidumping: How it Works and Who Gets Hurt*, Ann Arbor, University of Michigan Press.

FINGER, J.M. and FUNG, K.-C. (1994), 'Will GATT Enforcement Control Antidumping?', in *Journal of Economic Integration*, Vol. 9, pp. 198-213.

FINGER, HALL and NELSON (1982), 'The Political Economy of Administered Protection', in *American Economic Review*, pp. 452-466.

HOEKMAN, B. (1995), *Trade Laws and Institutions, Good Practices and the WTO*, World Bank Discussion Papers 282, 106 p.

MESSERLIN, P.A. (1991), 'The Uruguay Round Negotiations on Antidumping Enforcement', in P.K.M. Tharakan (ed.), *Policy Implications of Antidumping Measures*, Elsevier Science Publishers B.V., North Holland, Amsterdam, pp. 45-76.

RYCKEN (1991), 'Some specific issues in the antidumping proceedings of the European Communities', in P.K.M. Tharakan, *Policy Implications of Antidumping Measures*, North Holland, Amsterdam, pp. 191-271.

SCHUKNECHT, L. (1992), *Trade Protection in the European Community*, Harwood Academic Publications, Reading, 227 p..

THARAKAN, P.K.M. (1993), 'Contingent Protection: The US and the EC antidumping actions', in *The World Economy*, Vol. 16, No. 5, pp. 575-600.

THARAKAN, P.K.M. and J. WAELBROECK (1994), 'Antidumping and Countervailing Duty Decisions in the E.C. and in the U.S.: An Experiment in Comparative Political Economy', in *European Economic Review*, No. 38, pp. 171-193.

THARAKAN, P.K.M. (1995), 'Political Economy and Contingent Protection', *Economic Journal*, pp. 1550-1564.

VANDENBUSSCHE, H. (1996), 'Is European Antidumping Protection against Central Europe Too High?', in *WelwirtschaftlichesArchiv*, Vol. 132 (1), pp. 116-137.

VERMULST, E.A. (1987), *Anti-dumping Law and Practice in the United States and the European Communities*, North-Holland, Amsterdam.

VERMULST, E.A. and WAER, P. (1991), 'The Calculation of Injury Margins in the European Communities' Antidumping Proceedings', in *Journal of World Trade*, pp. 5-42.

5 Domestic Policy Variables and Foreign Direct Investment Inflows in Latin America

Willy Van Ryckeghem[1]

5.1 INTRODUCTION

The recent upsurge in foreign direct investment (FDI) inflows in Latin America is generally credited to the renewed confidence inspired by improved macro-policies and market-oriented reforms which were implemented by a majority of Latin American countries in the latter part of the 1980's. Although foreign investment decisions must ultimately rest on micro-calculations comparing expected rates of return to the opportunity cost of capital, an improved investment climate created by a favorable macro-economic policy environment is likely to positively influence growth and profit expectations, and thus the level of capital inflows[2]. This chapter reports on an empirical test of this hypothesis using a pooled regression technique for the seven largest Latin American economies during the period 1970-1992. The results show a significant impact of import liberalization, of depreciation of the real effective exchange rate and of deficit reduction of FDI. Finally, there would seem to be country-specific factors exerting a significant influence, independent of the macro-economic performance or -policies.

5.2 THE BASIC HYPOTHESIS: A FOREIGN INVESTMENT ACCELERATOR?

The research strategy which will be followed here consists of a stepwise pooled regression approach, under which we will try to establish the difference which macro-economic policies make to foreign investment by first estimating a function without policy variables, and next a function incorporating such variables.

Figure 5.1 FDI/GDP in Latin America

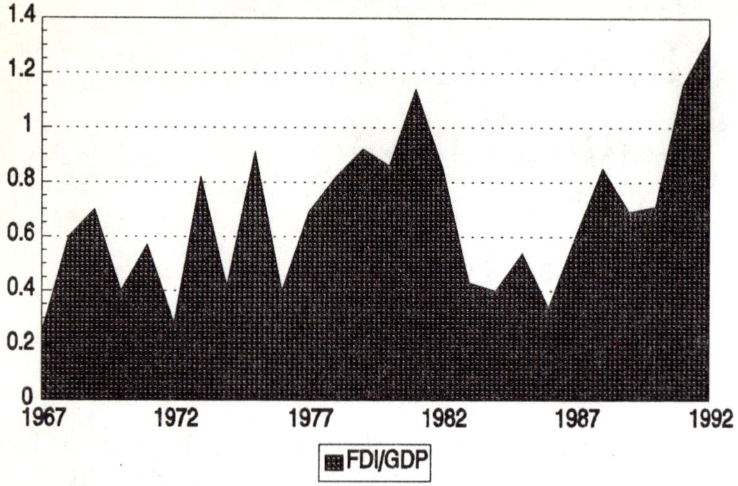

Source: IMF tapes and IDB estimates.

Relative to GDP of the seven major Latin American economies, foreign direct investment shows an upward trend, although with major fluctuations which seem related to the growth cycle of the region (Figure 5.1). The starting point of our multiple regression equation without policy variables is therefore the hypothesis of a foreign investment accelerator (cfr. Van Ryckeghem, 1966). This would establish a relationship between the level of FDI which a country attracts and the past increase in its GDP, or alternatively, between the FDI/GDP ratio and the immediately past growth rate of real GDP:

$$\$FDI/{*}GDP(t) = a + b\ GRGDP(t\text{-}1) \qquad [1]$$

In order to allow for possible scale effects (large countries receiving proportionately more foreign investment because of the size of their market), we add to the previous specification the natural logarithm of the level of GDP:

$$\$FDI/\$GDP(t) = a + b\ GRGDP(t\text{-}1) + c\ ln\ R\$GDP(t) \qquad [2]$$

We also want to test for any remaining systematic inter-country differences by introducing dummy variables for six of the seven countries:

$\$FDI/\$GDP(t) = a + b\ GRGDP(t\text{-}1) + c\ ln\ R\$GDP(t) + d\ D2 + \ldots + i\ D7$ [3]

At the same time, we want to examine the possible substitution effect between foreign direct investment and national investment:

$*FDI/\$GDP(t) = a + b\ GRGDP(t\text{-}1) + c\ ln\ R\$GDP(t) + d\ D2 + \ldots + i\ D7 + j\ \$NINV/\$GDP(t)$ [4]

Confirmation of the postulated negative sign of national investment would imply that in periods when national investment is low, additional room is created for foreign investment, and vice versa (crowding out effect).

The results are reported in Table 5.1 (equations 1-4). They can be summarized as follows:

1. A small but usually significant positive accelerator effect is found to exist with a coefficient varying from 0.02 to 0.04. By itself, this factor accounts for only a very small proportion of the variance in the dependent variable, however.
2. The results are improved substantially when we incorporate a market size effect as represented by the level of constant dollar GDP. This confirms the conclusions of both micro- and macro analyses of the determinants of FDI (cfr. Agarwal, 1980).
3. After taking into account the effect of market size, we tested the effect of any remaining country-specific factors through the use of country-dummies. Only the dummy variable for Venezuela had a significant (negative) impact, indicating that FDI flows to this country are systematically lower by approximately half a percentage point of GDP than those to the rest of Latin America.
4. The results suggest the existence of a small but significant degree of substitution between foreign direct investment and national investment. Introducing this factor doubles the influence of the accelerator effect and improves its significance.

Although all the variables introduced so far have statistically significant coefficients, together they still explain only 16 percent of the total variance in the FDI to GDP ratios. This probably reflects the presence of large random measurement errors in the FDI statistics at the individual country level.

Visual inspection of the time series shows a see-saw pattern of the time series which would seem to confirm this hypothesis.

5.3 THE IMPACT OF MACRO POLICIES

The introduction of additional variables which are a reflection of policy measures approximately doubles the explanatory power of the equation (cfr. Table 5.1). Not only are the coefficients of the policy variables usually statistically significant, but the significance of the other variables is also improved. The two variables that most contribute to this dramatic improvement are the real effective exchange rate and import liberalization.

$FDI/$GDP(t) = a + b GRGDP(t-1) + c ln $RGDP(t) + d D7 - e $NINV/$GDP(t) + f ln RER(t-1) + g $M/$GDP(t-1) + h DEF/GDP(t-2) *[5]*

The real exchange rate, defined in a way that it goes up when a currency undergoes a real depreciation, was introduced with a one year lag to avoid a possible problem of simultaneity (possible feedback effect from FDI inflows to currency appreciation). The coefficient has the expected sign and is statistically significant.

The contribution of the lagged import coefficient is particularly important. Again, a one year lag was imposed in order to avoid the feedback effect from foreign direct investment on imports of the same year. The problem with this variable is that it overstates the importance of import liberalization, since it implicitly assumes that the import coefficient is normally a constant, and that all deviations from this constant can be ascribed to trade policy.

Visual inspection reveals a strong inverse relationship between the import coefficient and the real exchange rate (see Figure 5.2 for case of Argentina). Since the real exchange rate is already included as a separate explanatory variable in our equation, we decided to 'clean' the import coefficient of its influence by subtracting the estimated impact obtained by a separate simple regression. Only in the case of Chile, where no such impact could be measured, did we maintain the original observations of the import coefficient. The results obtained with the thus corrected import ratios reflect a reduced, but still highly significant impact on the FDI/GDP ratio.

Table 5.1 Regression results: Dependent variable: Foreign direct investment period: 1970-1992.

Equation	(1)	(2)	(3)	(4)	(5)	(6A)	(6B)	(7)	(8)
Coefficients:									
Constant	0.48	-2.41	-2.16	-1.53	-3.35	-6.78	-4.35	-4.87	-4.84
	(5.68)	(-2.62)	(-2.39)	(-1.72)	(-2.91)	(-5.45)	(-4.13)	(-4.77)	(-4.83)
GDP growth rate (lagged 1 year)	0.02	0.02	0.02	0.04	0.03	0.03	0.03	0.02	0.02
	(1.96)	(1.96)	(1.90)	(3.05)	(2.67)	(2.55)	(2.65)	(1.74)	(1.48)
GDP in constant US$ of 1988		0.26	0.25	0.27	0.24	0.47	0.45	0.53	0.51
		(3.16)	(3.03)	(3.48)	(3.00)	(5.54)	(5.24)	(6.21)	(6.03)
DVEN			-0.52	-0.32	-0.49	-0.87	-0.83	-0.88	-0.83
			(-2.63)	(-1.61)	(-2.35)	(-4.24)	(-3.98)	(-4.37)	(-4.22)
National Investment				-0.04	-0.03	-0.04	-0.03	-0.04	-0.03
				(-3.40)	(-2.25)	(-2.87)	(-2.59)	(-3.05)	(-2.17)
Real Eff. Exchange Rate (lagged 1 year)					0.46	0.49	0.38	0.27	0.14
					(2.43)	(2.84)	(2.12)	(1.54)	(0.76)
Imports (lagged 1 year)						0.06			
						(5.32)			
Imports adj. by LRER (lagged 1 year)							0.05	0.05	0.04
							(4.82)	(4.35)	(3.56)
Budget Deficit (lagged 2 years)								-0.05	-0.06
								(-3.72)	(-4.20)
PRIV									0.49
									(2.65)
R**2	0.02	0.08	0.12	0.18	0.21	0.34	0.32	0.37	0.40
R-BAR**2	0.02	0.07	0.10	0.16	0.19	0.31	0.29	0.35	0.37

Figure 5.2 Argentina 1970-1992: Imports/GDP and the real exchange rate

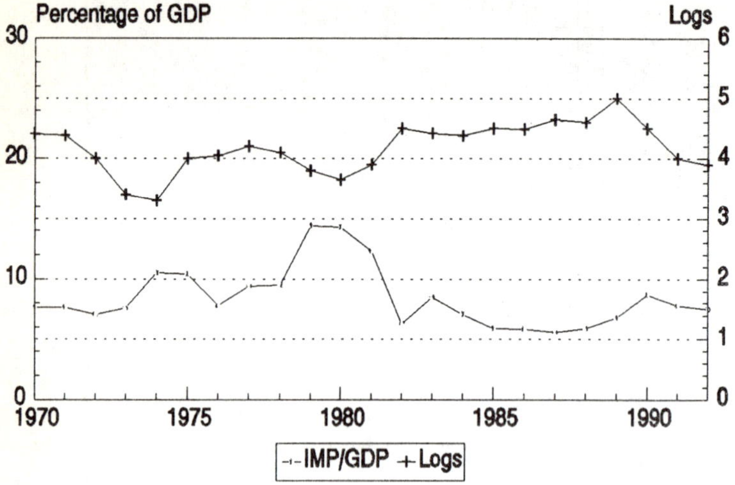

Source: IDB estimate

The public sector deficit, somewhat inadequately represented here by the central government deficit, which is the only concept for which a complete set of time series is available, is shown to have a negative impact on foreign direct investment. The most significant results are consistently obtained with a time lag of 2 years, although this occurs at the expense of the influence of the real exchange rate, which loses in significance.

Finally, in order to allow for the special role which the privatization process has played in recent years in attracting foreign direct investment, we introduced a separate dummy variable, which takes on the value one for the period when privatization took place, and zero for the rest of the time. It appears from the results that privatizations account on average for half a percentage point of GDP for the countries where they took place.

To conclude, we want to draw attention to a comparison between the calculated and the observed dollar values for total Latin American FDI. Both the overall trend and the fluctuations around it are captured quite well (R-square of 0.72) by the calculated values, given the fact that the estimated equation was specified in relative terms to GDP and not in absolute amounts.

A graphical inspection of the residuals of this simple regression signals systematic negative residuals for the period of the debt crisis (1983—87), and zero or positive ones for the more recent years. This suggests that while the policy variables represented in our equation satisfactorily capture the swing in attitude towards Latin America on the part of foreign investors since 1987, they do not adequately account for the dramatic drop in confidence which occurred during the debt crisis. We tested this hypothesis by regressing the above mentioned residuals against a country risk variable, which measures the credit rating provided by leading international banks[3]. No significant relationship was found to exist, however, between the residuals and this country risk variable, neither at the aggregate nor at the individual country level. This somewhat surprising result is confirmed by alternative trials using debt service ratios as a proxy for country risk. Our interpretation for the residuals is therefore that they represent an over-reaction to the debt crisis which characterized much of the decade of the eighties.

5.4 SOME FURTHER RESULTS

The recent upsurge in FDI inflows as well as of other capital flows in Latin America is generally credited to the market-oriented reforms and improved macro-policies which were since implemented by a majority of Latin American countries. These reforms include import liberalization, real exchange rate depreciation, removal of public sector deficits, privatization of public enterprises, financial liberalization and, thus confirming the link between treatment of MNEs and overall development strategy, flexibilization of foreign investment regulations.

In this part, we present further results obtained with an additional year of observations (1993) for the same set of countries. In addition we also somewhat broaden the specification by using a more appropriate definition of the openness in the economy.

5.4.1 The model without policy variables

The specification without policy variables confirms the existence of a foreign investment accelerator as well as the presence of a positive scale factor, reflecting the fact that large economies tend to receive proportionately more foreign investment. Our sample of observations remains limited to the seven largest economies of Latin America (Argentina, Brazil, Chile, Colombia, Mexico, Peru and Venezuela), which traditionally account for approximately 90% of total FDI in the Latin American region.

A comparison of the new results with the earlier ones yields the following picture:

$$\text{OLD: } \$FDI/\$GDP(t) = -1.53 + \underset{(3.05)}{0.04\ GRGDP(t-1)} + \underset{(3.48)}{0.27 \ln R\$GDP(t)} - \underset{(-1.61)}{0.32\ DVEN}$$

$$\underset{(-3.40)}{-0.04\ \$NINV/\$GDP(t)} \qquad R2 = 0.18 \quad R2cor = 0.16$$

$$\text{NEW: } \$FDI/\$GDP(t) = 0.21 + \underset{(5.05)}{0.07\ GRGDP(t-1)} + \underset{(2.10)}{0.16 \ln R\$GDP(t)} - \underset{-(3.25)}{0.59\ DVEN}$$

$$\underset{(-5.20)}{-\ 0.07\ \$NINV/\$GDP(t)} \qquad R2 = 0.29 \quad R2cor = 0.27$$

The estimate of the foreign investment accelerator is now almost twice as high as in the earlier result (0.07 vs. 0.04), and also statistically more significant. Although the absolute size of this coefficient may still appear small, we have to bear in mind that the share of FDI itself seldom represents more than one percent of Latin American GDP, so that the contribution of an acceleration in growth of, say 2 percentage points, would be modest but far from negligible (+ 14% increase in FDI).

On the other hand, the coefficient of the scale factor seems much more important. Note that the specification implies decreasing returns to the size of the economy, in terms of increased FDI. According to this new result, the fivefold difference in size between the economies of Brazil and Venezuela, would account for half a percentage point difference in the shares of FDI in each country's GDP, whereas the tenfold difference in size with Peru would account for 0.7 percentage points difference in FDI. When adding country dummy variables to the equation, our original results only found the coefficient for the Venezuela dummy to be systematically negative. The new results confirm this finding, and indicate that Venezuela receives approximately 0.6 percentage points of GDP less in foreign direct investment than could be expected on the basis of its structural characteristics alone.

Table 5.2 Regression results: Dependent variable: Foreign direct investment as a percentage of GDP (1970-1993)

Equation	(1)	(2)	(3)	(4)	(5)	(6)	(7)	(8)	(9)	(10)	(11)	(12)	(12A)	(13)
Coefficients:														
Constant	1.00 (8.34)	4.36 (7.17)	4.20 (6.99)	5.29 (8.51)	3.14 (5.10)	5.34 (8.38)	5.48 (8.74)	3.79 (4.12)	3.14 (3.33)	3.08 (3.30)	3.32 (3.49)	3.47 (3.64)	3.19 (3.36)	2.74 (8.13)
GDP growth rate (lagged 1 year)	0.05 (2.32	0.04 (2.09)	0.04 (2.15)	0.05 (2.80)	0.07 (4.36)	0.10 (6.51)	0.10 (6.42)	0.10 (6.55)	0.10 (6.52)	0.08 (6.57)	0.08 (5.55)	0.08 (5.32)	0.08 (5.50)	0.08 (5.54)
GDP in constant US$ of 1988		0.33 (5.63)	0.31 (5.31)	0.41 (6.82)	0.23 (3.96)	0.23 (4.29)	0.24 (4.65)	0.11 (1.43)	0.06 (0.76)	0.03 (0.35)	0.06 (0.71)	0.07 (0.91)	0.05 (0.59)	
DVEN			-1.19 (-2.98)	-1.26 (-3.27)	-1.13 (-3.28)	-0.57 (-1.77)	-0.60 (-1.91)	-0.65 (-2.09)	-0.63 (-2.05)	-0.74 (-2.40)	0.70 (-2.27)	-0.68 (-2.19)	-0.68 (-2.21)	-0.72 (-2.36)
DPRY				-1.45 (-4.68)	-0.92 (-3.23)	-0.90 (-3.47)	-1.06 (-4.10)	-0.75 (-2.65)	-0.64 (-2.25)	-0.64 (-2.26)	-0.65 (-2.32)	-0.59 (-2.09)	-0.68 (-2.36)	0.63 (-2.68)
DITO					2.27 (8.02)	1.66 (6.13)	1.44 (5.26)	1.60 (5.75)	1.68 (6.03)	1.63 (5.91)	1.64 (5.95)	1.62 (5.89)	1.68 (6.16)	1.70 (6.84)
National Investment						-0.11 (-7.24)	-0.10 (-6.16)	-0.11 (-6.67)	-0.11 (-6.90)	-0.12 (-7.28)	-0.12 (-6.92)	-0.11 (-6.68)	-0.12 (-6.94)	-0.12 (-7.52)
Real effective exchange rate (lagged 1 year)							0.76 (3.22)	0.69 (2.96)	0.65 (2.77)	0.56 (2.42)	0.52 (2.23)	0.55 (2.36)		
Imports (lagged 1 year)								0.02 (2.49)						

Table 5.2 Cont.

Equation	(1)	(2)	(3)	(4)	(5)	(6)	(7)	(8)	(9)	(10)	(11)	(12)	(12A)	(13)
Imports adj. by LRER (lagged 1 year)									0.03 (3.26)	0.03 (3.23)	0.03 (2.93)	0.03 (2.52)	0.03 (2.92)	0.03 (5.11)
Budget Deficit (lagged 2 years)										-0.04 (-2.85)	-0.04 (-2.84)	-0.04 (-2.75)	-0.04 (-2.90)	-0.04 (-2.97)
PRIV											0.26 (1.22)	0.29 (1.37)	0.25 (1.18)	
LREALW (lagged 2 years)												-0.37 (-1.56)		
L(REALW/REER) (lagged 1 year)													-0.44 (-2.09)	0.47 (-2.30)
R**2	0.02	0.13	0.16	0.23	0.39	0.50	0.52	0.53	0.54	0.55	0.55	0.56	0.55	0.55
R-BAR**2	0.01	0.12	0.15	0.32	0.38	0.48	0.50	0.51	0.52	0.54	0.54	0.54	0.54	0.54

The extended sample also confirms the existence of a substitution effect between FDI and national investment, which is highly significant and now almost twice as important as in the earlier results. Introduction of this variable also helps to raise the significance of the foreign investment accelerator (t-value of 5).

The existence of a possible substitution effect between FDI and national investment may come as a surprise those who are expecting to find complementarity between both variables. To the extent that the growth rate of the economy impacts positively on both national and foreign investment, one would indeed expect both variables to rise or fall together. Our result is not in contradiction with such a hypothesis, however. What it indicates is that for a *given growth rate* of GDP any shortfall in national investment would be made up by additional foreign investment and, conversely, any excess in national investment would reduce the incentive for foreign investment to come into the country. Our results are also consistent with those obtained by Fry (1993) in a study for the World Bank in which he found a significant negative coefficient when he regressed the domestic investment ratio to GDP against that of foreign investment for a worldwide sample of countries. It should be noted, however, that in Fry's study the causal relationship runs in the opposite direction (foreign investment crowding out domestic investment, rather than vice versa), and that in his specification foreign investment is included in domestic investment, whereas in our study FDI is netted out of domestic investment to arrive at the definition of national investment. The overall explanatory power of the specification using exclusively only structural factors now reaches 29% of the total variance of FDI as compared to only 18% in our earlier results.

5.4.2 The model with policy variables

Although foreign investment decisions by individual firms must ultimately rest on micro-calculations comparing expected rates of return to the opportunity cost of capital, a favorable macro-economic policy environment is likely to positively influence growth and profit expectations, and thus the level of capital inflows. Starting in 1990 capital flows to Latin America in recent years show a clear shift in emphasis from public sector borrowing and capital flight from the private sector to major reflows to the private sector, either as foreign direct investment, portfolio investment and other short-term and long-term lending to the private sector. This reversal in capital flows to the private sector is generally attributed to the policy reforms which were implemented in Latin America in the second half of the eighties, and which involved opening up of the economies, reducing public sector deficits, starting the process of privatization, and correcting overvalued exchange rates (cfr. Table 5.2).

Deficit reduction and privatization are shown to have a positive impact on foreign direct investment. The coefficients of the general government surplus and that of a privatization dummy, which takes on the value one during years of substantial privatization and zero for the rest of the period, are almost identical to those obtained in the first part of this paper. The only difference is that the government surplus now appears with a one-year lag rather than the somewhat unrealistic two-year lag found earlier.

The major difference with the first part of this paper is the treatment of the foreign sector. In the original version, we introduced the import/GDP ratio as a proxy for import liberalization (after correction for real exchange rate variations).

Following the suggestion of several commentators, we now broaden this variable to the degree of openness of the economy, as represented by the ratio of total trade (exports *plus* imports) to GDP. This presents the advantage that a correction for real exchange rate variations is no longer necessary since the real exchange rate supposedly impacts with opposite signs on imports and exports.

Trade and foreign direct investment interact in various ways. The import liberalization of recent years presented an additional attraction for foreign direct investment that is export-oriented. This would explain why more open economies have tended to attract relatively more foreign direct investment. At the same time, FDI by itself has stimulated imports, in particular of capital goods. FDI is also closely related to the phenomenon of intra-trade between the different establishments of the same transnational firm.

Finally, a competitive exchange rate is generally accepted to exert a positive influence on FDI-decisions: not only does it enhance the purchasing power of foreign capital when it enters the country, but it also provides insurance against sudden sizeable real devaluations in the future. In our earlier results, the estimate of the coefficient of the real effective exchange rate was approximately 0.14, indicating that a hundred percent real depreciation would result in an increase in the FDI/GDP ratio of 0.1 percentage points, which is a rather modest impact.

OLD: \$FDI/\$GDP(t) = -4.84 + 0.02 GRGDP(t-1) + 0.51 ln R\$GDP(t) - 0.83 DVEN
(1.48) (6.03) -(4.22)

- 0.03 \$NINV/\$GDP(t) - 0.06 DEF/GDP(t-2) + 0.49 PRIV + 0.04\$M/\$GDP(t-1) +
-(2.17) -(4.20) (2.65) (3.56)

+ 0.14 ln RER(t-1) *R2= 0.40*
(0.76) *R2cor=0.37*

The real wage level, however, is equally important as the exchange rate in determining a nation's competitiveness. When we combine both variables in order to obtain a wage cost variable corrected for movements in the real exchange rate, we do obtain a coefficient of similar magnitude with the correct negative sign, and an improved t-value although still not significant at the 95% significance level:

NEW: \$FDI/\$GDP(t) = -2.96 + 0.06 GRGDP(t-1) + 0.39 ln R\$GDP(t) - 1.00 DVEN
(4.67) (4.99) (-5.31)

- 0.07 \$NINV/\$GDP - 0.04 DEF/GDP + 0.36 DPRIV + 0.02 \$(X+M)/\$GDP - 0.13 ln(RW/RER)
(-5.16) (-3.49) (2.36) (3.91) (-1.19)

R2 = 0.48
R2cor= 0.45

This final result explains 45% of the variance of the dependent variable, as compared to 37% in the earlier result.

5.5 SUMMARY AND OUTLOOK

In summary, it can therefore be concluded that foreign investors like to invest in countries that:

- grow rapidly,
- have a big domestic market,
- have a low public sector deficit,
- privatize,
- are relatively open, and
- are competitive in terms of real wages and real effective exchange rates.

None of these conclusions should come as a surprise. The importance of the results lies rather in the quantification of the effects: what they tell us is that if Latin America were able to accelerate its average growth rate by 2 percentage points, reduce its fiscal deficit by 2 percentage points of GDP, increase both exports and imports by 2 percentage points of GDP, continue to privatize, and improve its competitiveness index by 10 percent, the ratio of FDI to GDP could be expected to increase by approximately 30 per cent. On the other hand, if growth were to drop by 2 percentage points, deficits were to rise by 2 percentage points of GDP, exports and imports were to fall by 2 percentage points of GDP, privatization were to come to a halt and competitiveness were to deteriorate by 10 percent, the ratio of FDI to GDP could be expected to fall by 70 per cent. The reason for the asymmetry in this result is the privatization dummy, which is maintained at its current value (1) in the positive scenario, but which drops to zero in the negative scenario.

The outlook for foreign direct investment for the rest of the decade of the 90s is mixed. It seems quite likely that most Latin American countries will consolidate the reforms initiated during the 80s and will maintain the positive investment climate created by the liberalization of FDI regulations and the privatization process. However, as the privatization process gradually exhausts itself in a number of countries, such as Argentina and Mexico, this special factor will tend to lose influence over time.

The decreased importance of privatization manifests itself in a temporary fall in FDI in 1995–96, from an annual level of more than $16 billion in 1993–94 to $12-13 billion in 1995–96. After this, the upward trend is resumed under the influence of overall growth of the Latin American economies (the accelerator effect) and the continuation of policies that are generally favorable for foreign direct investment[4]. This trend will be further strengthened by the widening process of hemispheric integration, especially through the likely accession to NAFTA of other Latin American nations. To the extent that this process is reflected in rising import-to-GDP ratios, it can be expected to make a powerful contribution to the longer-term expansion of foreign direct investment in Latin America.

Symbols

FDI = foreign direct investment
GDP = gross domestic product
GRGDP= Growth rate of real GDP
NINV= national investment (=domestic investment-FDI)
DVEN = Venezuela country dummy variable
DPRIV= dummy variable for privatization
DEF = general government deficit
X= exports
M= imports
RW= real wage index
RER= real exchange rate index (goes up when the currency depreciates in real terms)

When the variable is preceded by a $ sign, it means the corresponding amount is expressed in current US dollars. When it is preceded by R it means it is expressed at constant prices; e.g. R$ means constant dollars of a given base year.

NOTES AND REFERENCES

1. Inter-American Development Bank, Washington DC. Valuable research assistance by Ivan Guerra and Fernando Quevedo is gratefully acknowledged. Helpful comments and suggestions were received from J. Bergsman, B. Kosacoff, H. Glesjer, S. Lall and F. Larrain.
   A more complete version of this paper was published as CIMDA (Centre for International Management and Development-Antwerp) Discussion Paper, No, 1995/E/20, University of Antwerp (Belgium)
2. Most recent authors on the subject of FDI recognize the need to establish a unified theory. For further references, see the bibliography.
3. These ratings are published twice a year by *The Institutional Investor* and are available for the period 1979-1992.
4. In order to avoid subjective biases in this scenario, we selected the values of the independent variables from the latest WEFA forecast for the seven Latin American countries included in our forecasting equation. See WEFA (1993).

BIBLIOGRAPHY

AGARWAL, J. (1980) 'Determinants of Foreign Direct Investment: A Survey', *WeltwirtschaftlichesArchiv*, vol. 116 no 4.

BEETZ, C. and W. VAN RYCKEGHEM (1993) *Trade and Investment Flows between Europe and Latin America and the Caribbean*. Seminar on Latin America's Competitive Position in the Enlarged European Market, Hamburg.

CARDOSO, E. and R. DORNBUSCH (1989) 'Foreign Private Capital Flows' in H. Chenery and T.N. Srinivasan (eds). *Handbook of Development Economics*, vol. II, Amsterdam, North Holland.

EATON, J. and T. AKIKO (1994) *Bilateralism and Regionalism in Japanese and U.S. Trade and Direct Foreign Investment Patterns* IED Discussion Paper Series, Boston University, July 1994.

EDWARDS, S. (1990) *Capital Flows, Foreign Investment, and Debt-Equity Swaps in Developing Countries*, NBER Working Paper no 3497.

FINANCE AND DEVELOPMENT (1992) *Recent Trends in FDI for the Developing World*, vol. 29, March.

FRY, M. (1992) *Foreign Direct Investment in a Macroeconomic Framework: Finance, Efficiency, Incentives and Distortions*, University of Birmingham, International Finance Group Working Paper (UK) no IFGWP-92-17:1-30.

FRY, M. (1993) *Foreign Direct Investment in a Macroeconomic Framework*. Policy Research Working Papers, The World Bank, May 1993.

GUBITZ, A. (1990) *Impact of Investment Policies on German Direct Investment in Developing Countries: An Empirical Investigation*, Seventh Conference of the European Association for Research in Industrial Economics, Lisbon.

Inter-American Development Bank (IDB) and Institute for European-Latin American Relations (IRELA) (1993) *Foreign Direct Investment in Latin America and the Caribbean: An Overview of Flows from Europe. Japan and the United States, 1979-1990.*

International Monetary Fund (IMF) (1992) *Report on the Measurement of International Capital*, September, Washington, D.C.

LEON-ASTETE, J. and C. OLIVA (1992) 'Components no-estacionario pardad del poder de compra en doce paises latinoamericanos' in *Cuadernos de Economia*, Santiago de Chile, December.

LIZONDO, S. (1990) *Foreign Direct Investment* International Monetary Fund Research Department, Washington D.C., IMF Working Paper W//90/63.

Naciones Unidas (CEPAL) (1992) *Inversión Extranjera Directa en América Latina y el Caribe 1970-1990*, Simposio de Alto Nivel sobre la Contribución de las Empresas Transnacionales al Crecimiento y el Desarrollo de América Latina y el Caribe. Santiago de Chile, octubre.

OMAN, C. and O. DE BARROS (1991) *Trends in Global FDI in Latin America*, presented at the Inter-American Dialogue meeting in Washington DC, mimeo, December, 18-20.

ROOT, F. and A. AHMED (1979) 'Empirical Determinants of Manufacturing Direct Foreign Investment in Developing Countries', *Economic Development and Cultural Change*, vol. 27, no 4, July.

SECCHI, C. (1992) *Factors Influencing Private Investment (Including Domestic Investment and FDI) in Argentina*, mimeo, Bocconi University.

TURNER, P. (1991) *Foreign Direct Investment in the Developing World: the Experience of the 1980s* Bank for International Settlements, Basle, January.

VAN RYCKEGHEM, W. (1966) 'Un Modelo de Intercambio y Desarrollo', *Desarrollo Económico*, enero-marzo 1966, Buenos Aíres, Argentina, pp. 427-433.

WEFA (1993), Latin American Economic Outlook, June.

6 The Global Economy, National Governments and Supranational Economic Regimes

John H. Dunning

6.1 INTRODUCTION

The theme of this chapter is based on two simple, but important, propositions. The first is that the advent of the global economy[1] is requiring national governments to reappraise their domestic macro-organizational policies[2]; and, in doing so, to take a more systemic approach to the implementation of these policies. It is also demanding reconsideration of the role of supra-national regimes, e.g. GATT, the World Bank, IMF and the UN, particularly as fashioners and sustainers of a level playing field for international competition. The second is that, if individual countries are to fully embrace the challenges of the global marketplace, their governments need both to appreciate the nature of the new international division of labour and to take more constructive and coordinated action to help cross-border markets to work efficiently.

Neither of these propositions necessarily implies that there should be less government – or that governments should not 'get off industry's back'. Nor does it mean they support the view that governments should intervene more in the decision-taking process of the wealth creators of society, *viz* business enterprises. But what they do mean is that governments should openly acknowledge that, as an organizational mechanism, markets are *not* a free good; they cost resources to set up, to operate and to maintain. They also mean that governments need to recognize that the efficiency of many markets – and particularly those supplying products for global customers – is not solely determined by the transactions of the buyers and sellers in those markets, but by a host of other factors, including the actions taken by other governments, over which they may have no immediate influence or control. They mean that governments, like firms competing in the global marketplace, need to reexamine their organizational structures and administrative regimes; and to concentrate on only those activities which, relative to the private sector, they are best able to undertake. And finally, they mean that in times of disturbingly high structural unemployment, and as governments seek to attract the highest possible share of the world's 'quicksilver' resources of capital, technology and managerial skills to their territories, the role of supra-national regimes, authorities and institutions may need to be re-examined if the playing fields of the global competitive game are to be kept reasonably level.

6.2 THE NATURE OF THE GLOBAL ECONOMY

One of the main features of the emerging global economy is the close structural interdependence between the constituent nations in the trade of goods and services, and in the movement of assets and people. A typical global *firm* will own or control subsidiaries, and engage in value-added business alliances and networks in each continent and in each major nation state. It will source its inputs of manpower, capital, raw materials and intermediate products from wherever it is economic to do so; and it will sell its goods and services in each of the main markets of the world. Similarly a *country* which is fully open to the forces of globalization is likely to be geographically diversified in its financial trading and investment relationships; and for the value added associated with these relationships to constitute a significant part of its gross national product (GNP)[3].

The distinction between an international and a global economy is partly one of the *scope* of cross-border transactions (e.g. the number of countries a firm invests in and/or the proportion of its sales accounted for by the foreign subsidiaries), and partly one of the *organization* and *ownership* of the transactions. Economists like to distinguish between 'shallow' and 'deep' integration, the latter indicating a much more intimate, extensive and mutually beneficial interdependence between the transacting parties than the former. At one time, the main avenue for commerce was arm's length trade — the most shallow form of integration. In the closing years of the twentieth century, this is no longer the case. In the last decade or so, the deep integration forged by multinational enterprises (MNEs) and a host of cross-border strategic alliances and other forms of inter-firm cooperation have replaced trade as the main forms of international transactions.

According to the Transnational Corporations Division of UNCTAD, the growth of direct investment in the period 1980-1992 rose 1-1/2 times faster than trade, and twice that of world GDP (gross domestic product); further details are set out in Table 6.1. There are now up to 37,000 companies which between them own or control 200,000 foreign affiliates. The number of cross-border strategic alliances runs into tens of thousands; and the number of subcontracting agreements into hundreds of thousands. The majority of these arrangements also involve MNEs. Indeed, such companies also account for about 70% of world trade; and about the same proportion of privately financed R&D. Trade, direct investment and alliances are all inter-connected in an increasingly complex web of transactions; and although labour services and most natural resources and the finished products of firms continue to be bought and sold on the open market, an increasing proportion of intermediate goods and services, e.g. telecommunications and financial services, are produced and traded either within the same MNEs or networks of firms in which MNEs play a dominant role.

Globalization is then leading to structural fusion of economic activities between the nations of the world. Nowhere are its effects more strikingly seen than in the organization of financial markets. As Walter Wriston (1992) has astutely observed:

> The new world financial market is not a geographical location to be found on a map, but, rather, more than 200,000 electronic monitors in trading rooms all over the world[4].

Another observer, Richard O'Brien (1992) has put it even more succinctly by describing global financial integration as 'the end of geography'. At the same time, 'keiretsu' type networks are now spreading from Japan to the US, Europe and Asia. For example, more than 150 first tier suppliers of the major Japanese auto producers have already moved into the US and Europe. Science parks and industrial districts are mushrooming, particularly in the Triad countries. Throughout the world, the 1990s are seeing the emergence of a new form of international capitalism — what some scholars are aptly calling *alliance* capitalism[5] —, an essential feature of which is the

Table 6.1 World-wide foreign direct investment and selected economic indicators, 1992 and growth rates for 1981 - 1985, 1986 - 1990, 1991 and 1992 (Billions of dollars and percentages)

Indicator	Value at current prices, 1992	Annual growth rate (per cent)			
		1981-1985	1986-1990	1991	1992
Foreign direct investment outflows	171	3	24	-19	-10
Foreign direct investment stock	2,200	5	11	12	9
Sales of foreign affiliates of transnational corporations	4,800	2	15	-13	--
Current gross domestic product at factor cost	23,300	2	9	4	5
Gross domestic investment	5,120	0.4	10	4	5
Exports of goods and non-factor services	4,500	-0.2	13	3	--
Royalties and fees receipts	37	0.1	19	8	5
Strategic alliances (annual average)	327	258	388	297	395

Source: UNCTAD, Programme on Transnational Corporations, based on IMF, balance-of-payments tape, retrieved on 13 December 1993; UNCTAD, Programme on Transnational Corporations, *World Investment Directory*, volume VI, *Global Volume* (Geneva, United Nations, forthcoming) unpublished data provided by the World Bank, International Economics Department and data kindly provided by MERIT (Maastricht) in high technology strategic alliances.

complementarity between the cooperative activities of economic agents and the competitive market economy.

6.3 WHY GLOBALIZATION?

At this juncture, it is worth reminding ourselves that globalization is just one feature of some major changes now taking place in the world economy. Exhibits 6.1 and 6.2 identify some of these which have had (or are having) particularly significant implications for business enterprises and national governments — and, no less important — on the interactions between them.

Exhibit 6.1 The emerging global environment as seen by national governments

- Renaissance of the market system.
- Growing structural integration of the global economy.
- Enhanced mobility of wealth creating assets.
- Increasing number of countries approaching 'take off' stage in development
- Convergence of economic structures among advanced countries and some industrializing countries.
- Changing criteria by which governments are evaluating FDI (foreign direct investment).
- A better appreciation by governments of the costs and benefits of inbound and outbound international business.

Exhibit 6.2 The emerging global environment seen by firms

- Increasing need to exploit global markets (e.g. to cover escalating R&D costs).
- Competitive pressures to procure inputs (raw materials, components, etc.) from cheapest possible sources.
- Regional integration has prompted more efficiency seeking FDI.
- Growing ease of trans-border communications and reduced transport costs.
- Heightened oligopolistic competition among leading firms.
- Opening of new territorial opportunities for FDI.
- Need to 'tap into' foreign sources of technology and organizational capabilities; and to exploit economies of agglomeration.
- New incentives to conclude alliances with foreign firms.
- Changes in significance of particular locational costs and benefits.
- Need to better balance the advantages of globalization with those of localization.

Most of these features are self-evident. Key among the changes, as they are perceived by *governments* are:

(a) The renaissance of the market system — as is most dramatically being played out in Central and Eastern Europe, China and India.

(b) The emergence of new sources of market outlets and of competition from some developing countries — particularly in East Asia; and the convergence of living standards and economic structures among advanced industrial countries.

(c) A better appreciation by governments, both in developed and developing countries, of the contribution which trade, FDI and cross-border strategic alliances by MNEs can play in fostering competition and upgrading national resources and capabilities.

From the perspective of *firms*, we would especially emphasize:

(a) The rising costs of innovatory activities, the interdependence of many new technologies and the more rapid rate of obsolescence of products. These events are compelling corporations, particularly in technology and information intensive sectors, to conclude strategic alliances with other firms, both to speed up the innovatory process and to seek out new markets.

(b) The spectacular improvements in trans-border communication facilities — including super information highways — brought about by quite spectacular technological innovation.

(c) The need to tap into foreign sources of technology and organizational competencies; yet, at the same time take account of localized supply capabilities and consumer needs.

(d) The change in significance of the particular costs and benefits which affect the locational choice of firms. In particular, traditional supply variables, e.g. unskilled labour and raw material costs, are today much less important than once they were; while those to do with the behaviour of competitors and the availability of government-related location-bound capabilities, e.g. an educated work-force and a first-rate transport and communications infrastructure, which are complementary to the core competencies of firms, are becoming more important.

6.4 A PERESTROIKA OF WESTERN GOVERNMENTS?

Let us consider some of the implications of these characteristics of the emerging global environment for the policies of national governments. We shall concentrate on the macro-organizational, rather than on the macro-economic policies of governments — primarily because we believe that it is the former where the recasting of government actions need to be most focused in the next few years. One reason for this belief is that a substantial part of the unemployment now plaguing Western economies is the outcome of technological advances and structural changes rather than that arising from inappropriate domestic macro-economic policies.

Figures 6.1 and 6.2 distinguish between the ingredients of macro-economic and macro-organizational policies[6]. For the most part, it has been the former which have engaged the attention of scholars in recent years. Yet, it is our contention that as the international economy becomes structurally integrated, the freedom of action for distinctive national macro-economic policies is being reduced. By contrast, the ability of individual governments — by their actions or non-actions — to affect the form and composition of the economic activity undertaken within their national boundaries is growing rather than receding; and it is the reason for this, and the consequences of this, with which this chapter is concerned.

Of the various characteristics of the globalizing economy, to which we have already alluded, we shall focus on seven; and, for each of these we suggest how they may impinge on the macro-organizational actions of governments. Some of these characteristics are more obvious than others. Some are more controversial than others. Clearly, the response of national governments to these characteristics will depend on a range of country-specific factors — most noticeably on the cultures and institutions; and space does not allow us to enlarge upon any of the 'bullet' points we shall make. But, this chapter will have achieved its purpose if it can persuade the reader that globalization *does* require national governments to reappraise their role as custodians of their citizens' economic welfare; and to reconsider the way which they manage their affairs.

Figure 6.1 Realms of economic governance

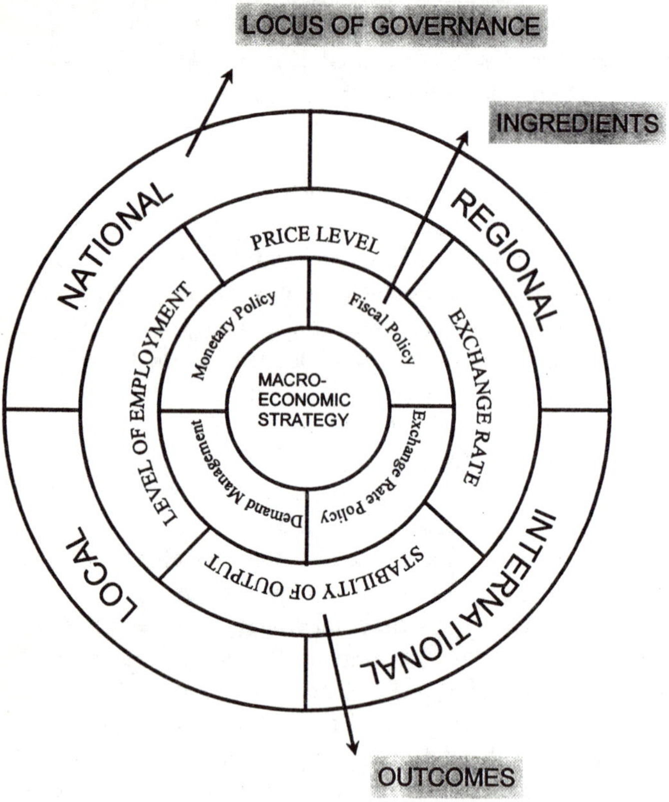

Figure 6.2 Realms of economic governance

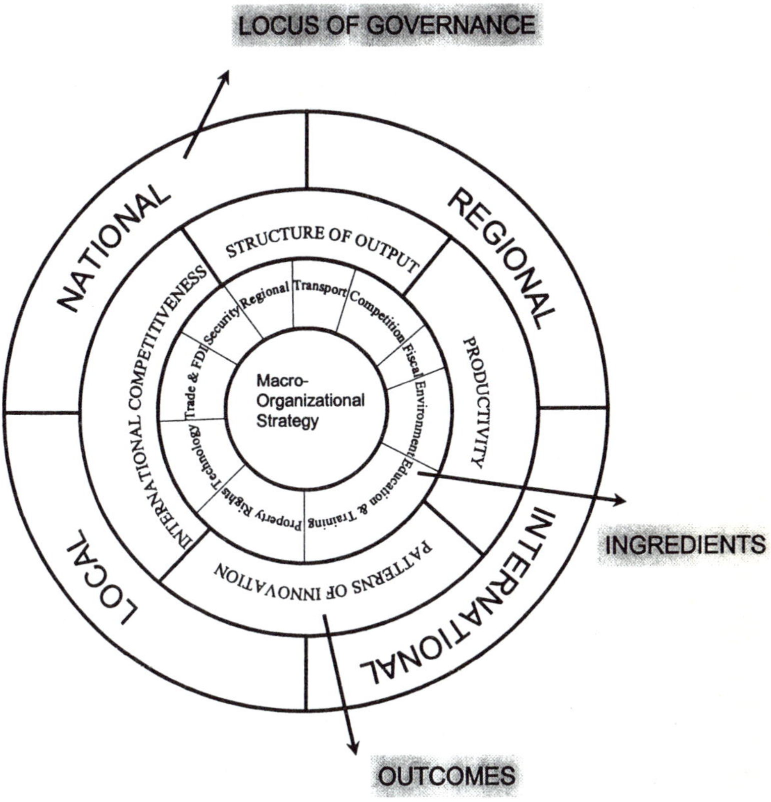

Let us now make our seven observations:

(1) In today's global economy, many — though not all — wealth creating assets, notably people, money and knowledge, move much more freely across national boundaries than once they did[7]. It follows, then, that national government actions, based upon the presumption that all the wealth creating resources and capabilities necessary are locked within national boundaries, may be inappropriate in the age of MNEs, and of cross-border cooperative alliances and networking. Both individuals and firms are increasingly able to respond to unwelcome government actions by 'voting with their feet'. The theory of competing governments is more alive today than it has ever been.

(2) A country's stock of wealth-creating assets in most industrialized countries today is not made up of *natural* endowments, e.g. land and unskilled labour, but rather of accumulated physical capital, human knowledge, learning and experience. In an innovation led market economy resources have to be *created*, and continually nurtured and improved if they are to meet stringent demands of global capitalism. This suggests that governments which do not ensure that the capabilities of the physical and human resources located within their territories are optimally used and upgraded will find that their firms will be out-competed in the global marketplace.

(3) The kinds of products now being produced in modern industrial society are requiring new forms of economic organization. As future demand and supply conditions become more uncertain, yet individual markets become more interdependent, single firm hierarchies are being increasingly complemented or replaced by cooperative ventures and inter-firm networks. Increasingly, too, market transactions are yielding benefits and/or costs to economic agents, beyond those engaged in the exchanges, i.e. the externalities of markets are becoming more important. The implication of this statement is that governments need to recognize that if they are to perform their tasks efficiently, both the market system *in toto* and many individual markets require a legal and institutional infrastructure, and a particular culture on the part of its participants. Moreover, in spite of advances in information technology for many dynamic products, these costs are increasing. The market is best regarded as a public good;

and as such, governments have a duty to cooperate with the participants in the market and to help make it work. This role of government might be called a *market enhancing* role to distinguish it from an interventionist, and a hands-off role of government.

(4) In the 1990s, many trading nations are increasingly competing with each other for global resources, capabilities and markets. For most of the last one hundred years, countries have primarily bought and sold *different* goods from each other; and engaged in complementary, rather than competing economic activities. This is no longer the case — at least not in the industrialized world. Most of the trade of developed nations is with other developed nations, which produce and sell similar goods and services. Moreover, most contemporary trade in manufactured goods and services is *intra-industry* trade. In a very real sense — and especially in times of global unemployment —, nations compete with each other for labour creating and competitiveness enhancing mobile assets. From this it follows that their governments need to appreciate that competition between their firms and those of other countries is increasing, and that, in their efforts to raise national productivity in a structurally integrated global economy, they need to take account of how well their location-bound resources and capabilities are performing relative to those of their main foreign competitors[8].

(5) Governments are not only competing with each other like firms; they are increasingly taking strategic competitive postures in their economic policies. For example, although much depends on the individual markets served, Britain's main competitors in the 1990s are Germany, France, the US, Italy, Japan and increasingly the newly industrial countries of the Far East. In so far as government actions (of the kind we have already described) affect the ability and motivation of firms from these countries to be competitive; and in so far as each government may be affected by the other's economic strategies, it is possible to perceive of some governments as strategic oligopolists. The implication of this statement is that governments need to acknowledge that their macro-organizational strategies may impinge on those of other governments, and that these, in turn, may impact on the effectiveness of their own strategies.

(6) Increasing productivity is assuming rising importance in the priorities of many governments. For the last 40 years, it has been at the top of the political agenda of Japan; it is now central to the economic strategies of the US, the UK and many countries in Europe. This is partly because the global economy is bringing about more competition between firms and countries; but also because unless firms and countries strive to become more productive, they are in danger not just of failing to increase their standards of living, but of facing reduced standards of living. Thus, governments which fail to place increasing productivity at the top of their political agenda risk not being able to achieve many of the social goals for which they are striving. This is because the realization of these goals involves sustaining the competitiveness of their firms and location bound resources in global markets. For most industrial countries, raising productivity is no longer an optional luxury; it is an essential ingredient of any economy whose firms are producing goods and services which firms from other countries are producing, and which are competing for similar markets.

(7) Because of technological and other developments, there is an increasing interdependence between the various functions and tasks of governments. Moreover, to be effective, the domestic macro-organizational role of governments needs to be much more *holistic* and coordinated than it has been in the past. All too frequently, the functions of different government departments have been treated as if they were self-contained. But in so far as each directly or indirectly affects competitiveness in the global marketplace, and each involves a strategic response on the part of governments, it is important that each is seen to be part of an integrated strategy. Large MNE enterprises are increasingly recognizing that a systemic approach to the way in which they organize their resources is essential if they are to remain internationally competitive. But, at the same time they are becoming less hierarchical and more heterarchical in their organizational structures. Governments should learn from corporations, and seek to restructure their systems of governance so they may cope better with the demands of a global economy. In particular, they need to flatten the pyramidal structure of governance and decentralize managerial responsibility.

If the above seven observations are correct, then it should follow that governments which follow a well-orchestrated and systemic, market oriented economic strategy, and those which share the responsibility of decision taking with their leading constituents, are likely to be the most competitive. And this, in fact, is what scholarly research shows — even though there is no correlation between the extent of interventionism by governments and economic progress (Ostry, 1993). From this, it follows that tax policy cannot be isolated from innovation policy; that innovation policy cannot be separated from environment policy; that education policy cannot be divorced from tax policy, and so on. In truth, in today's global village, national governments are responsible for organizing a network of different but interrelated activities to meet a common set of objectives.

What then is the issue? It is simply that the kind of systemic and strategic approach to the management of a country's assets we have advocated requires a different culture and structure of internal governance than one which is oriented to achieving a variety of objectives, each of which is assumed to be largely independent of the other. It also needs a different approach towards the functions of particular departments, dealing the ingredients of macro-organizational strategy identified in Figure 6.2. The current practice of Western governments is to treat each of these as competitors for the resources available to (or acquirable by) governments, with the final decision of 'who gets what,' usually being taken at Cabinet or the equivalent level. To this extent, the locus of decision taking resembles a hierarchical structure of a firm in which the heads of different product or functional areas bid for resources to pursue their own objectives, the outcome of which is decided by the Board of Directors. Figure 6.3 (a) illustrates this 'hub and spoke' approach.

The 'strategic systemic' approach suggests a network of relationships both between a central body responsible for the formation and outcome of macro-organizational strategy and individual areas responsible for advising on and implementing that strategy, and between these areas. Figure 6.3 (b) sets out this 'spider's web' approach to governance. This resembles much more a heterarchical system of decision taking, in which there is a complex web of lateral, as well as vertical decision taking relationships.

Figure 6.3 Two kinds of intra-government administration

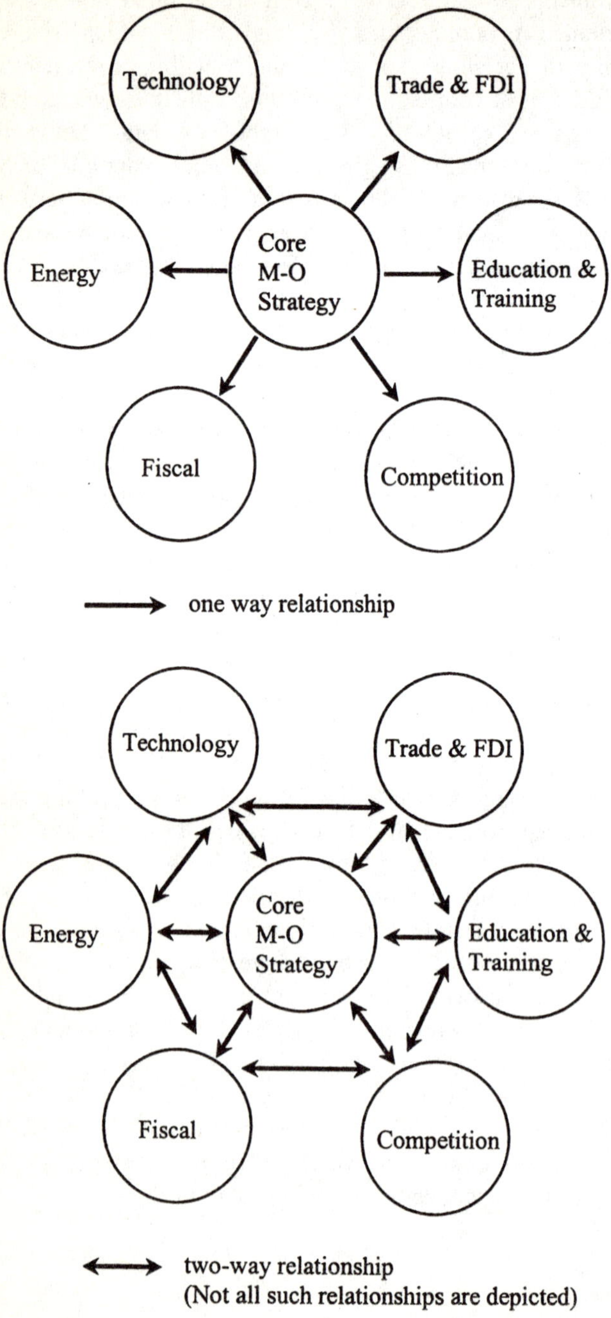

While each department continues to press for resources to promote its own particular goals, the final allocation of resources is decided — in part at least — on its perceived effect on the governments' core macro-organizational strategy[9].

The other aspect of macro-organizational policy which requires reappraisal is that of the relationships between governments. If, as we have suggested, governments are increasingly being compelled to behave as strategic oligopolists, in the sense that the actions of any one government may affect the welfare of corporations or citizens in other countries, and this will trigger off a reaction of their government, it follows that this may require modification to their earlier strategies. These are of two kinds. The first is a genuine strategy to promote competitiveness and reduce endemic market failure, and the second is to try to reach an international accord for a level playing field, and to penalize structural distorting policies taken by any one national government. Both of these strategies may necessitate organizational changes in the way intra-governmental decisions are taken.

The global economy is then demanding a 'perestroika' of government. There is a need to recognize that just as scale manufacturing and Fordism is becoming an outdated method of organizing work so the kind of governance appropriate to a Fordist environment is inappropriate. And, just like the emerging organizational structures of large and successful firms, those of governments need to be lean, flexible and anticipatory of change. National administrations also need to dramatically improve their public image. The new paradigm of government behaviour should eschew such negative or emotive sounding words like 'command', 'intervention', and 'regulation', and replace them by such words as 'empower', 'steer', 'coordinate' and 'cooperate'.

At the same time, we would not wish to imply that actions taken by national governments to promote economic prosperity and growth are costless, or that such actions are necessarily the most efficient way of achieving that objective[10]. However, it is possible to identify the kind of situations which favour government intervention of one kind or another. Exhibit 6.3, which is derived and adapted from Robert Wade's (1988) evaluation of the role played by national administrations in fostering the economic development of Japan, Taiwan and Korea sets out some of these situations, and the ways in which they may help reduce the transaction costs of governance.

Exhibit 6.3 Some examples of situations in which governments might successfully contain their own organizational costs

Intervention or form of government intervention	Consequences for the reduction of government related transaction costs
• The enhancement of national competitiveness by market facilitating measures; and publicly promoting this objective.	• Reduces effectiveness of rent seeking special interest groups. • Increases work effort of public agents. • Makes policy trade-offs easier to identify and solve.
• The containment of interventionist policies to activities severely hampered by market failures.	• Clarifies policy makers task and reduces problem of bounded rationality.
• A holistic approach to the coordination of complementary policies and institutional mechanisms.	• Reduces likelihood of sub-optimization. • Captures economies of scope in governance and increases intra-organizational information flows and learning.
• An ethos of consensus and cooperation between private and public policy makers, e.g. with respect to mutually beneficial goals and the means by which goals can best be achieved.	• Reduces transaction costs of interaction between representatives of private and public sector. • Increases knowledge of public decision takers. • Reduces chance of uninformed or biased media coverage in forcing governments into ill advised or hasty decisions.

• The recruitment of the most talented and well motivated individuals for public sector employment, e.g. by offering competitive working conditions and encouraging initiative and entrepreneurship.	• Likely to inhibit the pursuance of sub-optimal goals and to reduce bounded rationality and opportunism and use of inefficient production technologies.
• The insulation of the policy making process from the strongest (and most undesirable) pressure groups.	• Reduces the effectiveness of rent seeking by special interest groups, and relieves the policy making process from the pressure of day to day politics.
• The presence of a national ethos or mentality of the need to be competitive and create wealth. Partly, this embraces a 'commutarian' culture and partly one which encourages personal initiative, entrepreneurship, scientific specialization and competition.	• Favors coordination of strategies and policies of public and private organizations and reduces the sub-optimization problem in the public sector.
• The absence of strong sectoral interest groups, e.g. farmers and left-wing labor groups, which might press for interventionist measures by governments other than those which are market facilitating.	• Reduces possibility of ideological conflicts and undue emphasis being placed on the redistribution of incomes as a (short term) social good.

Sources: Adapted from: Wade, R. (1988) Stiglitz, J. (1989) Grestchmann, K. (1991) Hämäläinen, T. J. (1994)

While the data in Exhibit 6.1 are fairly self explanatory, and provide a set of guidelines for governmental intervention, they have not yet been subject to rigorous scrutiny by scholars. The globalizing economy may well enhance the need for such a scrutiny, as it increases the costs of misinformed or inappropriate government action.

6.5 SUPRANATIONAL ECONOMIC REGIMES

For the final paragraphs of this chapter, we would like to address some of the implications of globalization for existing supranational regimes of polity. If our thesis that national governments are increasingly competing with each other for resources, capabilities and markets to maintain or increase the living standards of their citizens is correct; and, if, *de facto*, such competition tends to be oligopolistic, then, there is a real danger that the strategic rent seeking measures taken by individual governments might lead to a situation not unlike the 'beggar my neighbour' trade policies of the inter-war years. For the last forty years, GATT has helped set the rules of the game for trade. But, today the playing field of international competition is structured very differently. As we have already observed, and as Figure 6.2 has sought to show, it embraces a whole range of policy options open to governments, each of which may affect the capabilities of a nation's firms to trade and compete with each other, just as much as the conditions underlying trade *per se*.

And, it is in pursuance of industrial, innovation, taxation, competition and environmental strategies to advance *national* economic interests where the level of the international playing fields is currently the most uneven.[11] Moreover, it is erroneous to suppose that, by itself, the global market economy will iron out these differences. Again, *inter alia*, because of their unique business cultures and institutions, different countries have different interpretations of the justification for, and fairness of, government intervention. To give just one example — the continuing dialogue between Japan and the US on market access seem to get bogged down so easily because of the different interpretations by the negotiators of the legitimacy of their respective governments trade-related measures.

It is, perhaps, worth reminding ourselves that inter-government cooperation on non-economic matters dates back many years. Agreements on technical standards, weights and measures, and meteorological systems were all first concluded in the last century. However, the idea that supranational regimes, authorities and institutions may be an appropriate means of governing *economic* activity is relatively new, and is still very controversial. But, two things should be said. The first is that it is becoming increasingly difficult to distinguish between what is and is not an economic activity. For example, each of the examples of politico-market failures we have just described, affect, in some way of other, the infrastructure of modern economic activity. The second is that the emergence of the global economy, alliance capitalism and the widening competing interface between governments, is forcing a reappraisal of our attitudes towards the role of transnational economic regimes.

The next decade — as alliance capitalism evolves and the world moves towards multi-polar, rather than hegemonic, politics — there is likely to be much talk about refashioning the role of international institutions such as GATT, the World Bank, IMF and the UN. In particular, the agenda for the newly formed World Trade Organization (WTO) is already being widened to include such issues as competition policy, the environment and labour standards. Indeed, some observers have argued that it is time for a new global economic order to replace the international economic order of the 1960s and 1970s. But, before that is a feasible proposition, many questions need to be answered about the adequacy of existing regimes. Exhibit 6.4 identifies just a few of these.

From an economist's viewpoint, the efficacy of supranational regimes, be they publicly or privately financed or managed, rests on whether they promote and sustain the efficiency of resource allocations more effectively than other organizational forms — including national governments, groups of firms, individual firms and markets. We have suggested that just as hierarchies or inter-firm alliances might help lower the transaction and coordination costs of markets, and the actions taken by national governments might reduce the same costs of hierarchies or inter-firm alliances, so supranational action might help reduce the costs of structurally distorting behaviour by national governments. Of course, multinational institutions — notably some international cartels — may themselves behave in a structurally distorting way, but, in cases where they make for a more efficient international allocation of economic activity, they help advance rather than inhibit global welfare.

At the same time, in regional and international debating chambers, the role of national governments in championing their own causes will continue to be a critical one. But, just as we have argued, the kinds of restructuring of the organization of markets and firms demanded by globalization is compelling national governments to redesign their world of governance; so, too, the functions and authority of international institutions may need to be reconsidered if globalization is to offer the fullest possible benefits which a free exchange of people, goods and services demands.

Exhibit 6.4 Questions which need to be asked about the adequacy of supranational regimes in a global economy

- What aspects of the organization of economic activity are best coordinated at an international level; and, how is this changing with the advent of the global economy?
- In what way do the existing supranational institutions need to be revamped to better accommodate the needs of the structural integration of the world economy?
- How can newly emerging institutions like the European Bank for Reconstruction and Development (EBRD) be accommodated into the existing scheme of things?
- What are the appropriate rules or regimes for managing the world economy?
- Should international coordination aim to promote economic convergence or diversity and specialization?
- Is the current organizational structure of international institutions suited to the needs of the twenty-first century?
- What form should policy coordination take and how should it be policed in an age of alliance capitalism?
- To what extent should there be more jointly shared responsibility between supranational institutions and private firms?

NOTES AND REFERENCES

1. Defined as an economy in which there is close economic interdependence among and between the leading nations in trade, investment and cooperative commercial relationships; and where there are relatively few artificial

restrictions on the cross-border movement of people, assets, goods or services.

2. Sometimes called micro-economic strategies; but we prefer to limit this term to the actions of individual firms and consumers.
3. Significance in this context is difficult to define as the internationalization ratio of a country, e.g. as measured by the ratio of trade or foreign direct investment to its GNP, will obviously vary with the size of the country. For example in 1990, the trade to GDP ratio varied between 202.32 for Singapore and 102.35 for Belgium to 14.48 for Japan and 12.68 for the US. The FDI to gross fixed capital formation between 1986 and 1990 ranged from 19.65 in the case of Singapore and 16.65 for the UK to 2.03 for Japan and 1.09 for Brazil. However, for almost all countries, the ratios increased - and increased substantially - throughout the 1980s.
4. Wriston, W. (1992), as quoted in Kobrin, S. (1993).
5. See, for example Dunning, J. H. (1994a) and Gerlach, M. J. (1992).
6. As originally set out in John H. Dunning (1992).
7. Some of the implications of the increasing mobility of resources across national boundaries for US business and government policy are explored in McKenzie, R. and Lee, D. (1991).
8. This statement does *not* mean that governments should seek to ensure that all their firms are as competitive as their foreign counterparts in all activities, but simply that they are as competitive *as they can be, given the constraints of the location-bound resources which are inputs into the production process*. In other words, there is a little 'X' inefficiency in resource usage.
9. To illustrate, the decision on whether to allocate resources to building a major new highway would not be solely taken on the basis of the direct costs and benefits involved, but also on how the competitiveness of the nations, firms and location bound resources would be affected. Similarly, any proposal to change corporation tax should take account of the possible consequences of such tax changes on the locational decisions of its own and foreign MNEs.
10. Among the possible failures of direct government intervention to successfully overcome the deficiencies of the market, one might mention the rent seeking activities of powerful pressure groups; the magnification of market failures (e.g. with respect to the supply of environmental or social products) by the news media or other politically motivated interests; the inability of governments to attract the best talents (due *inter alia* to ineffective incentive systems); the lack of commercial expertise and bounded rationality of public decision takers; the pursuance of non-economic (especially ideological) goals by politicians; the inadequacy of market related performance indicators which may lead to the establishment of sub-optimal standards (e.g. with respect to budgets, investment and control of information flows); the high-time discount (or short-termism) of political decision takers; the lack of market pressures to minimize X inefficiency, especially in the case of public monopolies; uncertainties and

ambiguities inherent in the provision of goods and services, which are in the domain of governments, e.g. defense equipment, educational and health services; and the lack of a coordinated system of governance (cf. with that in case of private hierarchies); and the difficulty of adjusting policies and institutional structures to quickly meet the needs of technological and economic change.

11. For an analysis of some features of multinational governance in a global economy, and the system frictions it may generate in the cases of competition, research and development, foreign direct investment and financial market regulation, see Ostry, S., (1990).

BIBLIOGRAPHY

DUNNING, J.H. (1992) 'The Global Economy, Domestic Governance, Strategics and Transnational Corporations: Interactions and Policy Implications' *Transnational Corporations*, vol. 1, no 3 (December), pp. 7-46.

DUNNING, J.H. (1994a) 'Globalization, Structural Transformation and Development', The 6th Prebisch Lecture (Geneva: UNCTAD).

DUNNING, J.H. (1994b) 'Globalization: The Challenge for National Economic Regimes', The Geary Lectures 1993 (Dublin: Economic and Social Council).

GERLACH, M.J. (1992) *Alliance Capitalism*, (Oxford and New York: Oxford University Press).

GRETSCHMANN, K. (1991) 'Analyzing the Public Sector: The Received View in Economics and its Shortcomings' in F-X. Kaufman (ed.) (1991).

HÄMÄLÄINEN, T.J. (1994) *The Evolving Role of Government in Economic Organization* (Newark: Rutgers University) mineo.

HUGHES, H. (ed.) (1988) *Achieving Industrialization in East Asia* (Cambridge: Cambridge University Press).

KAUFMAN, F.-X. (ed.) (1991) *The Public Sector: Challenge for Coordination and Learning* (Verlin: Walter de Gruyter).

KOBRIN, S. (1993) *Beyond Geography: Inter-firm Networks and the Structural Integration of the Global Economy*, William Wurster Center Working Paper no 93 (Philadelphia: The Wharton School).

McKENZIE, R. and D. LEE (1991) *Quicksilver Capital: How the Rapid Movement of Wealth has changed the World* (New York: Free Press).

O'BRIEN, R. (1992) *Global Financial Integration: The End of Geography*, (London: Pinters Publishers).

OECD (1990) *Strategic Industries in a Global Economy* (Paris: OECD International Futures Program).

OSTRY, S. (1990) 'Beyond the Borders: The New International Policy Arena', in OECD (ed.) (1990).

OSTRY, J.D. (1993) *Selective Government Interventions and Economic Growth: A Survey of the Asian Experience and its Applicability to New Zealand*,

(Washington, D.C.: IMF Paper on Policy Analysis and Assessment PPAA/93/17).

STIGLITZ, J. (1989) *The Economic Role of the State* (Oxford: Bazil Blackwell).

WADE, R. (1988) 'The Role of Government in Overcoming Market Failures in Taiwan Republic, Korea and Japan', in H. Hughes, (ed.) (1988).

WRISTON, W. (1992) *The Twilight of Sovereignty* (New York: Charles Scribners and Sons).

7 Changing Perceptions of Foreign Direct Investment in Development

Sanjaya Lall

7.1 INTRODUCTION

This paper reviews some current views on the benefits of foreign direct investment (FDI) to developing countries and proposes the appropriate policies that they should adopt to transnational corporations (TNCs). It starts with emerging trends in the FDI scene of importance to developing countries. It then looks at the question of whether TNCs will, as is being proposed in some neo-liberal analyses of development, be the new "custodians of development". In this context it considers whether fully liberal policies on their entry should be recommended as a general strategy.

As we move into the second half of the 1990s, TNCs loom ever larger in the world economy. They account for increasing shares of world output, trade and technology. In 1991, it is estimated that TNCs and their affiliates generated total sales of $4.8 trillion and $1.5 trillion of intra-firm trade. This can be compared to total world trade in goods and services of $4.5 trillion including intra-firm trade ($3 trillion excluding it) (UNCTAD, 1994). The stock of FDI continues to grow faster than world GDP, domestic investment and trade. As far as the developing countries are concerned, the foreign investment scene has changed somewhat over the years since that survey was written. The volume and share of FDI to developing countries have risen significantly. Within this rise, the nature and direction of FDI have shifted a little, and there is growing differentiation among countries in terms of their participation in international production. For a large number of developing countries, some of the expectations held of its benefits have been found to be unrealistic. At the same time, others are benefiting greatly from TNC presence.

One of the most important changes is that the regime governing FDI has changed dramatically over the past decade. Many of the former concerns of developing country governments about the effects of transnational corporations seem to have evaporated. Governments now welcome FDI in a manner unprecedented in the history of economic development. The global shift of policy to market orientation and liberal economic policies has swept aside many of the erstwhile conventions and hesitations that formerly governed inward FDI. The belief that markets are essentially efficient (or at least more efficient than governments), and that TNCs embody the most developed forms of market efficiency, seem to go together, and TNCs are now proposed in many influential circles as the best and most effective way to transfer technology and promote new exports.[1] Bargaining with TNCs and the deliberate promotion of alternative modes of country-TNC relationships is frowned upon as undesirable intervention in largely efficient markets.

Yet many of the earlier economic arguments about the effects of TNCs remain unresolved. It cannot simply be *assumed* that the relevant markets work efficiently, and that there is no further need for policy interventions. Within developing countries there are evident market failures in the information, skill, capital and other markets within which industries and services function, and externalities and uncertainties mean that there may be valid arguments for the promotion of infant industries and the development of industrial capabilities.[2] Similarly, TNCs are the result of imperfect international markets for intangible assets. The imposition of internalised TNC markets on the deficient markets of developing countries can have ambiguous effects, since (as noted) what is beneficial for the enterprise is not necessarily so for society in the presence of market failures. It cannot be assumed, therefore, that non-interventionist policies on FDI or trade will automatically ensure that developing host countries maximise their static or dynamic economic benefits. This will be taken up later.

7.2 RECENT TRENDS IN FDI

This section reviews some of the main features of recent FDI in general and in developing countries in particular. It starts with general flows, then goes on to consider the composition, geographical distribution and mode of entry of international investments.

Figure 7.1. Flows of FDI, 1988-93 (US$ billion)

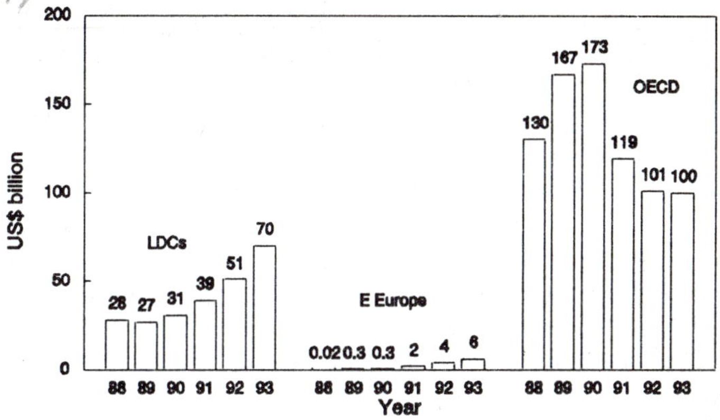

In terms of *overall trends* in foreign investments, the most significant recent feature of FDI is the rapid and sustained rise in flows to the developing world (see Figure 7.1). After a period of relative stagnation in the wake of the debt crisis and the ensuing recession up to the mid-1980s (in 1980–85 FDI to developing countries declined by 4% per annum), investment in the Third World revived strongly. Over the latter part of the '80s, it rose by 17% per annum, with a further acceleration in the 1990s. According to UNCTAD's *World Investment Report 1994*, total FDI to developing countries reached a record figure of $70 billion in 1993, an increase of 37% over the previous year. This rise followed increases (in current dollars) of 32% in 1991–92 and 25% in 1990–91, and the value of inflows to developing countries rose by 125% in the first 3 years of the decade.

This rise of investment interest in developing countries is striking not only because of the large sums involved but also because it reverses a decline in their share of total flows. This share had declined from the earlier peak of around one-third in the 1970s to one-quarter by 1980. It fell further to 16% in 1986–90, a period when FDI in the developed world rose rapidly (23% per annum).[3] In the 1990s, by contrast, there has been a sharp decline of inflows into the developed countries. In 1991, FDI in the OECD countries fell by 31%, and in 1992 by a further 16%. As a consequence, the share of developing countries reached its former peak of 33% in 1992, and went on to reach 40% in 1993. In current dollars, the value of FDI in the developing world was equal to that of inflows into the developed world in 1986. If present trends continue, direct foreign investment in the Third World will exceed that in the developed world in another two years or so. This would represent a major structural shift in the pattern, not just of investment, but also of the production and trade that arise from the investment.

How likely is such a structural shift? Is it merely a cyclical phenomenon? There are arguments on both sides. On the one hand, there are reasons to believe that the setback to the FDI in the developed countries is temporary. The developed world is still suffering from the overhang of a prolonged recession, from which recovery has been patchy and hesitant. In particular, the setback to FDI from Japan (which was at one stage the fastest growing investor overseas and seemed set to become the leading investor in absolute terms) has been a major factor in the global investment scene. When the recession does end, it is likely that FDI to OECD countries will revive. Moreover, the longer-term benefits of economic integration in Europe are likely to attract larger investment inflows. A revival of productivity growth in North America could open up new investment opportunities in high-technology industries. The gradual opening up of Japan to TNC activity could lead to a 'stock adjustment' in FDI there.

On the other hand, there *are* grounds to believe that there is some structural shift in investment flows towards (parts of) the developing world. A number of developing countries (the NIEs and the new-NIEs) have recorded sustained high rates of GDP growth, far higher than the developed world. This difference in growth performance and prospects is bound to attract larger investment flows to serve booming markets. Income growth reflects, in turn, an increase in their relative competitiveness in the production of goods and services across a wide range. The signs are that their competitive advantages will continue to grow as the NIEs upgrade their human capital base, technological capabilities and infrastructure and to move into more sophisticated technologies and services. At the same time, new competitors are emerging lower in the technology and skill scale, all with the ambition to emulate the success of the leaders. This dynamism and its spillovers (what the Asians refer to as the 'flying geese' pattern of growth) will attract more investments to serve export markets and integrated production networks.

The growing economic attractions of the developing world are enhanced by policy changes. Most developing countries are in the process of liberalising their investment regimes and opening up their capital markets. They are privatising state-owned enterprises, and often looking to foreign investors to buy large shares in such enterprises. There are many developing countries that are currently 'underinvested' in terms of their market and export potential, such as India and China. Considerable 'stock adjustment' can take place here, and what has already started there is of impressive proportions (see below).

Parts of Central and Eastern Europe should emerge as important destinations of FDI in the coming years if certain basic conditions (political stability, clear rules of the game, security, infrastructure and market access) can be established. These will challenge investment flows in the developed world, especially West Europe, more than in the developing world, though some diversion from the more advanced NIEs is also likely to occur. If we count CEE as part of the developing world (or, at least, not as part of the developed world), there is reason to expect a further structural shift away from the highly industrialised countries.

On balance, there are clearly both cyclical and structural forces at work. My own reading is that the latter will predominate. Thus, the ending of the recession will lead to renewed interest in the developed countries, but the share of the Third World is likely to continue to rise in the longer run. At least as far as productive sector investments (as opposed to investments in real estate and financial sectors) are concerned, investment flows to the latter are likely to exceed those in the former, not perhaps in the next two or three years but by the end of the decade.

As far as the *composition of FDI* is concerned, the trend away from the primary sector and into manufacturing and services continues. Within the latter groups, services seem to be gaining at the expense of manufacturing. Taking the major overseas investors, for instance: 51% of the USA's overseas investment in 1992 was in services, compared to 41% in 1985; for the UK, the figures are 46% and 35%, for Japan, 66% and 52%, for France 46% and 47% and for Germany 56% and 53% (UNCTAD, 1994). While much of service activity is concentrated in the developed world, there are clear signs that liberalisation has led to a substantial increase in service FDI in developing countries also. This is particularly marked in Latin America, where much of the recent revival of investment inflows has been in banking, telecommunications, hotels, retailing and similar activities. In Asia, the bulk of FDI still concentrates on manufacturing, testifying to the greater competitive capabilities built up there in industry. This difference in investment patterns deserves more interest than it seems to have received, since it may have differing implications for the longer-term development of the two regions.

The *geographical distribution of FDI* shows that concentration of TNC interest in a few more advanced developing countries continues, and has grown stronger in the very recent past. The ten largest recipients accounted for 76% of total flows into the Third World in 1992, up from around 70% in the preceding 10 years (but still below the 81% reached in 1981). These countries are shown in Table 1. The data presented are incomplete and not entirely reliable, but they are the best available (compiled by UNCTAD from IMF and OECD sources) and probably a good indicator of the rough magnitudes involved.

The most impressive growth in FDI inflows is into *China*, which attracted negligible amounts in 1981 but accounted for one quarter of all inflows to developing countries in 1992. In 1993 its dominance rose further, with actual inflows estimated at a massive $26 billion (not shown in the table). However, another estimate (by the securities firm Merrill Lynch) puts Chinese FDI *approvals* for 1992 at $58.1 billion, so that actuals are likely to be far larger than the figure given in the UNCTAD report. The same Merrill Lynch report shows that approvals by *India* in 1993 came to $2.9 billion, a major jump from the $200-300 million that was the norm for the previous several years. The growth in interest in these two giant economies was apparently diverting new investments from the new-NIEs like Malaysia (where approvals in 1993 declined by 60%), Thailand (by 68%) and Indonesia (by 4%).[4] If this is indeed a 'stock adjustment' in response to policy liberalisation and enhanced growth prospects, it may have a long way to go and may continue to suck away investment resources from other countries in the region. This raises interesting questions, but it is not possible to explore them in this paper.

The 47 *least developed countries* continue to be marginal to FDI flows, and in 1992 declined by 15% to a total of $300 million (0.6% of total flows to developing countries). Sub-Saharan Africa, in particular, received very little FDI. And this is despite widespread moves to liberalise foreign investment regimes and offer attractive incentives. Even countries undergoing strong structural adjustment programmes (like Ghana) failed to increase FDI inflows. There was a strong belief underlying these adjustments that 'getting prices right' and having liberal foreign investment was all that was needed to launch into East Asian style export-oriented industrialisation led by TNCs: this belief is now open to serious question.

Table 7.1 Ten largest host developing countries: Total FDI 1981–92 ($ billions)

Host country	FDI inflow	Host country	FDI inflow
China	33.8	Hong Kong	14.7
Singapore	33.0	Argentina	12.2
Mexico	29.0	Thailand	10.2
Malaysia	18.8	Egypt	7.8
Brazil	17.8	Taiwan	6.5

Source: UNCTAD (1994)

Clearly, the investment climate does matter, and in Sub-Saharan Africa it still probably needs to be improved. However, there is much more involved than 'opening up' to foreign trade and investment. These countries lack the economic fundamentals to launch competitive production in the newly liberalised trading environment. They lack, in particular, the technological, managerial and entrepreneurial capabilities to engage in competitive production in many modern industries (Lall, 1992.a). While structural adjustment has, often rightly, led to the abandonment of the high and indiscriminate levels of protection that formerly attracted TNCs into manufacturing, the new regime has failed to compensate with the creation of new skills and technological capabilities. Since the development of capabilities is a slow and costly process, this suggests that the least developed countries could hope to gain relatively little from FDI in secondary sectors in the foreseeable future.[5]

As far as the *mode of entry* of foreign investors is concerned, the rapid growth of global FDI in the late 1980s was fuelled in large part by cross-border *mergers* and *acquisitions* rather than by green-field investments. According to data collected by UNCTAD, some 57% of investments from the developed countries were in the form of acquisitions during 1986–90, reaching a peak of 68% in 1989 (UNCTAD, 1994). Thereafter, however, they declined. In 1990 acquisitions fell by 7% and in 1991 by a massive 55%, bringing the share of mergers and acquisitions in total FDI outflows from developed countries to 28%. Evidently the worsening environment for such activity was the main factor in the decline in FDI in the OECD countries.

The USA was the main target for cross-border take-over activity in the late 1980s, and $245 billion was invested there in that period in acquisitions. After 1990, however, the focus of take-over activity has shifted to Europe (mostly undertaken by European companies themselves), led by acquisitions in the UK. The 'single market' initiative has been an important incentive for such activity, as has more liberal government policies to foreign take-overs. This mode of entry is less common in developing countries, though some does exist, especially in Latin America.

Participation in *privatisation* has been another important mode of TNC entry (UNCTAD, 1994). Here, Latin America has the clear lead in the developing world. Between 1988 and 1992, $8.1 billion worth of FDI in Latin America took the form of the purchase of shares in public enterprises. This constituted 16% of total FDI in Latin America, and comprised 94% of total privatisation related FDI in the developing world. Central and Eastern Europe also attracted substantial inflows of this sort: in 1988–92 the value came to $5.2 billion, contributing 43% of total FDI in the region. Other developing regions relied much less on privatisation receipts. In East Asia the total sum involved was $377 million (and concentrated in the Philippines), accounting for only 0.7% of total FDI inflows; in South Asia the comparable figures are $52 million and 3% and in Sub-Saharan Africa $99 million and 1%.

By its nature, this mode of entry cannot be a sustained source of foreign investment. To the extent that it brings in fresh capital, technology and skills to enterprises in developing countries, and enables to compete better in open markets, FDI for privatisation is beneficial to the host countries. In addition, it may act as a 'signalling device' to TNCs, showing the commitment of the host government to private investment and foreign investors, and so may attract additional flows of FDI. However, to the extent that public enterprises are sold at undervalued prices, natural monopolies are not properly regulated, foreign buyers do not commit themselves to upgrading the enterprises purchased, and the investments attracted would have come in anyway, its economic benefits are more questionable.

Finally, it is worth remarking on a relatively new form of FDI that also involves opening up an area previously reserved for public investment: *infrastructure*. Many developing countries governments, faced with enormous demand for investment in roads, airports, ports, power generation and distribution, gas pipelines, telecommunication networks and so on, find their resources too limited. There is also a recognition that private groups can often deliver the product faster and run operations more efficiently if given the right incentives and a proper regulatory framework. Thus, a number of countries in Latin America and Asia (China, India, Malaysia, Pakistan, Indonesia and others) have allowed foreign entry into large infrastructure projects. The form of foreign participation has varied. Some projects have involved 'new' forms of investment, with BOT (build-operate-transfer) arrangements, where the foreign investor only has a short term interest. Others have involved longer-term interest, either joint ventures with the government or local private firms or foreign control in BOO (build-own-operate) arrangements. It appears that both forms of foreign participation will grow in the near future, as countries race to upgrade their infrastructure to compete more effectively in world markets.

7.3 SOME IMPORTANT ISSUES

Let us now turn to some features of recent FDI that may not be directly evident from available data, but are of interest to this discussion.

'New' forms of FDI[6] (minority-owned foreign ventures, licensing, management and other contracts and turnkey projects) are somewhat less in favour now that they were a decade ago. The shift to market-oriented policies has meant that fewer countries are laying down conditions on equity sharing by foreign investors. While there are sound economic and technological reasons for the growth of several 'new' forms, which will continue however liberal policies become, the emerging policy regime may lead to a reversal to classic forms of investment, with greater control exercised by TNCs.

The significance of low labour costs in attracting export-oriented FDI may be declining for the reasons mentioned above, though, given a minimum levels of skills and infrastructure, they still matter in a handful of low-technology activities. However, an important point should be noted here. The main industry still seeking cheap labour is low end garments, since semiconductors have become highly automated and capital-intensive. However, much of the recent spread of garment and textile production in the past decade or so was driven by the search for unused quotas, and it is not clear what effect of the impending abolition of the multi-fibre agreement (MFA) will have on the location of garment production. Some of the new producers may well have developed genuine competitive advantages, but others may disappear as unfettered competition emerges in the latter part of the 1990s. It is possible that producers like China (and possibly India), with low wages and substantial industrial capabilities, could destroy many other producers.

Of course, wages *per se* will remain an important competitive consideration in attracting export-oriented investments if all else is equal. The nature of international production is increasingly such that all else is less and less equal: thus, the pursuit of foreign investment (along with the industrialisation more broadly) will require greater domestic efforts at building the technological, organisational and other capabilities that are needed for world class production. This means that countries cannot wait passively for TNCs to lead them into industrialisation — they have to themselves undertake the investments and interventions that are needed to upgrade their capabilities.

While protected *domestic markets* are becoming less significant as attractors of FDI as countries liberalise, the attraction of large markets remains extremely important. Transnational enterprises continue to regard a production presence in important markets as vital for preserving their competitive edge. This is so for several reasons: *viz.* to bid for large contracts, maintain close relations with industrial buyers, win government approval, interact closely with consumers, tap local know-how and raw materials. Since liberalisation means that production facilities have to be efficient in world terms, however, the possession of large markets should now lead to different patterns of FDI from previous import-substitution regimes. For many large developing economies this may mean specialisation within the TNC framework in particular products or processes that feed into a system that spans several countries, what is referred to as 'integrated international production'.

As far as the more advanced developing countries are concerned, export orientation in this new setting may turn out to be rather different from the previous pattern of cheap-labour based production for TNCs. It is likely to involve a more even distribution of labour between countries, though developing countries are likely to be allocated tasks lower on the technology and skill scale than developed ones. As for the smaller and least industrialised countries, there may be a risk of being marginalised in the process of integrated production, at least as far as complex products and technologies are concerned. This is not to say that they will not attract FDI, only that the investments that come will be of stand-alone labour-intensive activities or of the simplest forms of assembly activity in vertically integrated operations (the pattern of export-oriented investments that was portrayed by Helleiner in his 1973 paper). This form of FDI, which flourished in the 1980s, is likely to reach a peak and decline as a proportion of TNC activity. It is also likely to become increasingly the preserve of Third World TNCs, particularly those from the East Asian NIEs.

A few words on the phenomenon of *'integrated production'* that has attracted attention recently (UNCTAD, 1993). Nearly all countries are becoming more closely involved with each other in economic and other terms, compelled by technological advance and a realisation of the benefits of such integration. However, it is TNCs that are leading the process of increasing economic integration. As UNCTAD (1993) between national economies by creating 'deep integration' between different units under their own control. Whereas the traditional TNC accorded a great deal of autonomy to affiliates, and exercised central control over only a few critical functions related to finance, intra-firm trade and allocation of production (what is referred to as 'shallow integration') (UNCTAD, 1993, pp. 158-165), there is an increasing tendency for TNCs today to extend corporate governance over a much wider functional area. Thus, the allocation of production is decided more on the basis of global division of labour rather than national market concerns; there is much more sustained and systematic exchange of products, parts and components within the firm; R&D functions are more integrated across affiliates; procurement and outsourcing are structured to serve the TNC as a whole; training is given on a more uniform basis; skills and know-how are transferred more intensively, and so on.

As the role of production under the aegis of TNCs grows, it appears that a country's participation in the international economy will be increasingly determined by its role in the integrated TNC system, at least in certain scale and technology intensive industries. The *internalised markets of the transnational are, in other words, replacing normal markets over a wider range of goods and services in a growing range of industries*. This form of deep integration is most advanced in the highly industrialised countries, and developing countries are only partially integrated at this stage. However, examples of integrated production in the more industrialised developing countries are easy to find.[7]

While such participation in the internalised markets of TNCs has obvious advantages in terms of allowing entry into activities with high initial barriers, providing access to advanced technologies and skills, and increasing export activity, the phenomenon is not entirely costless.

'Those trends suggest that host countries are likely to improve their productive efficiency and competitiveness. However, they may be less likely to build up their domestic technological capability. Integrated international production by TNCs can mean that host countries receive only a segment of an industry; the possibilities for the transfer of technology and skills may then be narrower than in the case of free-standing affiliates or simple integration' (UNCTAD, 1993, p. 176).

The issue of *intra-firm trade* retains its significance. In quantitative terms, the extent of such trade continues to grow unabated. Each new set of figures produced or cited suggests that ever larger proportions of world trade in goods and services are internalised within TNCs. Yet the monitoring and control of transfer pricing has practically vanished as a serious issue of policy in developing countries.[8] This is not mainly because their governments accept that they lack the capabilities to deal with transfer pricing, though this may well be true. It is more because any attempt at strict monitoring and control (say, at the level attempted by developed countries like the USA) would be interpreted as anti-TNC in spirit and so give the wrong signals to prospective investors.

There is no theoretical presumption that prices declared by TNCs (rather than set by them for internal management purposes) on their internal transactions would be optimal for the host economy. If declared transfer prices are geared to tax minimisation and other strategic purposes, it is quite likely that certain countries in which TNCs operate systematically lose revenue and local shares of profits to others. While a growing harmonisation of tax rates and other rules of the foreign investment game, and the desire of TNCs to be responsible corporate citizens are likely to have reduced the incentive to engage in aggressive transfer pricing, the danger always remains. The sheer magnitude of internalised trade is such that governments should remain aware of the risks involved and attempt to cope in ways that do not deter FDI. However, in the absence of significant progress in dealing with transfer pricing effectively this issue seems to be closed for the time being.

On the growth of *Third World TNCs,* it remains the case that in quantitative terms the established TNCs of the industrialised world continue to provide the bulk of the capital involved in international investment flows (though comparable data on investments by Third World firms are very difficult to get, particularly in East Asia). However, some developments within this broad picture are worth remarking on.

Third World TNCs are changing in character. While a substantial part of intra developing country investment in industry is accounted for by relatively small firms relocating low-technology, labour-intensive activities geared to export markets, a 'new breed' of large, capital-intensive and technologically sophisticated Third World TNCs is emerging, and investing in advanced activities the world over, especially from countries like Korea and Taiwan.[9]

The dynamism displayed by investors from the East Asian NIEs in recent years is amazing, and may well exceed expectations a few years ago. Well over half of the FDI flowing into China comes from the NIEs, mainly from Hong Kong followed by Taiwan, but also from other developing countries in the region.[10] While a part of the finance involved may come from developed countries, the evidence on the production and service activities of firms from these two NIEs suggests that most of the drive is local.

Increasing amounts of Third World investments are also coming in service activities like tourism, construction, banking and the like, as well as in infrastructure activities. Some of the largest BOT projects in China are undertaken by Hong Kong firms. A Malaysian telecommunications firm is undertaking projects in Indonesia and Vietnam. Korean construction firms are active in the entire region. And so on.

Let us now consider the issues raised by the inexorable growth in international and integrated production for the developing countries.

7.4 NEW CUSTODIANS OF DEVELOPMENT?

7.4.1 Theoretical approaches

Are TNCs about to become the new 'custodians' of development? Much depends on the analytical apparatus used to evaluate the effects on international investment. Helleiner's 1989 survey makes the point that the economic assessment of the welfare impact of TNCs on developing countries cannot be accomplished by the 'antiseptic analytics' of neoclassical economics. This point is more important than appears at first sight.

The current trend in neoclassical development economics is to believe that its analytical apparatus establishes that TNCs, *left to free market forces*, offer undiluted benefit to host countries. This belief is based on strong assumptions of market efficiency, under which the best policy regime is to 'get prices right' and liberalise fully on international trade and investment flows. One need only add considerations like the growth of international production, the acceleration of technological change and the shrinking of global economic space to argue that TNCs can be the 'custodians of development'. What better for sustained development than to attract the world leaders of production, trade and technology, when all their actions are by definition economically optimal?

While the 'custodian' role of TNCs can be derived from mainstream neoclassical theory it *is* based on strong assumptions: markets are fully efficient, and any failures that may exist are trivial or impossible to correct by governments. This is in fact the essential view held by the 'Washington consensus', and a growing and important view of development policy within the developing and donor countries. Clearly the 'custodian' role of TNCs is one that is widely believed in.

However, despite this powerful theoretical justification and despite the recent enthusiasm of developing countries to attract FDI, rigorous economic analysis suggests that the picture is more complex. The presumed absence of significant market has little justification in theory or practice. Market failures are rife in developing countries in the presence of missing markets, externalities, uncertainty and interlinked investments (Lall, 1994b). In their presence, an active role does remain in theory for governments to improve the allocation of resources. In practice, many governments have played just such a role, and have accomplished unprecedented economic success for their countries as a result.[11] The debate on industrial policy has much wider ramifications than for TNCs alone, but here also it has important implications. Note, however, that to question the welfare effects of TNCs in an untrammelled form is *not* to deny that TNCs will be an integral part of the development process, nor that their entry should be generally welcomed. The real issue is whether they serve as useful tools to be used by the 'custodians' or be left entirely to their own devices in the belief that markets are efficient (and private TNC interests do not diverge from those of host developing countries).

The empirical support for the neoclassical view of development is taken to be the experience of the East Asian NIEs. It is, therefore, instructive to take as an example the World Bank's recent, and much publicised, study of the East Asian economic 'miracle' (World Bank, 1993), touted as the most authoritative and objective account of the role of governments *vis à vis* markets in East Asia. Its conclusion is that the most that governments did was to be export oriented, provide a stable macro-economic setting, be 'open' to foreign technology and investment, and invest in human capital. This is described as a 'market friendly' role for governments and essentially conforms to established recipes of structural adjustment: get prices right, have good macroeconomic management and do not intervene in free market resource allocation. The encouragement of exports and education is taken to be non-selective, and any form on 'industrial policy' that seeks to promote particular activities over others is deemed uneconomic. While the role of TNCs is not explicitly analysed, it is implicit in the 'miracle' study and the Washington consensus that they play a key role in leading industrial development, especially in an export-oriented setting (as they are presumed to have done in East Asia). Certainly no intervention in international investment flows is seen to be justified; quite the contrary.

This sort of argument assumes away many of the market failures that are relevant to the analysis of development. It ignores the facts of economic development in East Asia and the real contribution of government intervention in the countries that have industrialised most successfully (Lall, 1994.a). It also skates over the fact that these countries (Japan, Korea and Taiwan) selectively intervened in different roles played by TNCs in different East Asian countries. Even within countries that depended heavily on TNCs, it ignores the crucial role of host governments in guiding foreign investment and extracting the maximum benefit by selective targeting and interventions. Let us start by outlining briefly why the textbook neoclassical treatment of market efficiency in the context of FDI is deficient.

7.4.2 Market efficiency and market failures

The literature on international investment attributes the existence of TNCs to the presence of failures in the markets for the intangible assets (technology, brandnames, skills, organisations, market access, privileged access to capital) that constitute their 'ownership advantages'. Without such advantages there would be reason for TNCs as an institutional form to come into being, and the essence of transnationalisation is the internalisation of imperfect intermediate markets. This itself weakens one of the foundations of the neoclassical approach, though it does not by itself create a case for interventions in the FDI process.

It may be argued, and indeed certain TNC authors have done so, that the internalised markets of transnationals are efficient not just for the firms but also for host economies. There is, in other words, no divergence between private and social interests, exactly the assumption of the neoclassical development economist. This cannot be justified if the requirements of efficient markets are not met, i.e. if there are missing markets, market power, externalities, uninsurable risk and uncertainty, interlinked investments and other such distortions. In this case, there is no presumption that the imposition of the internalised markets of TNCs will always provide *net* benefits to the host economy with its array of market failures. The potential benefits of TNCs are well known: they transfer some of their ownership advantages and so increase local skills, technology and production; they may have beneficial externalities for related buyers and suppliers; they provide competition for local firms; they may create additional exports; and some of the skills and knowledge they create may spill over to the rest of the economy.

Most of the potential costs of TNC presence in developing economies are also well known. Apart from deliberate practices like the use of transfer pricing and the exploitation of market power in local and foreign markets, which are not accorded much policy significance today and will not be considered here, they concern the impact of TNCs on the development of *local entrepreneurial and technological capabilities.* These remain the major outstanding issue concerning TNCs, and they are not something that can be readily evaluated by the analytical tools of neoclassical economics. The promotion of domestic capabilities is regarded as a non-issue by neoclassicals, an expression of nationalism that has no economic significance and addresses no market failures. Yet many developing countries have expressed this objective strongly in their policies. Have they been misguided?

A digression here into the analytical framework that supports the neoclassical view may be useful before we can answer such a question. The main problem in dealing with capabilities with neoclassical tools is that the basic theoretical approach of neoclassical economics has little or no role for capability development. In the standard neoclassical approach all markets are assumed efficient. Product markets give the correct signals for investment in new activities and factor markets respond to these signals. At the firm level, given perfect competition, information, foresight and efficient factor markets, the optimum point on the production possibility frontier is chosen according to prevailing factor prices. All firms are by definition equally efficient: technology is freely available, with full knowledge on techniques available to all firms — most importantly, it is costlessly and instantly absorbed, and any 'learning' process is known, predictable and automatic. Over time, as factor prices change to reflect changing endowments, their activities change accordingly — this represents the optimal pattern of specialisation and forms the basis for evolving comparative advantage.

Despite its obvious simplifications, this approach pervades the analysis and prescriptions of neoclassical development economics. It is under these assumptions that there is no reason to support the acquisition of capabilities by developing countries enterprises, since any necessary skills and information are instantaneously, costlessly and risklessly acquired. There are no infant industry arguments in this setting. There is also no reason to help *domestic* firms to build or deepen their technological capabilities, since information is not proprietary or tacit, and there is no cumulative process of investment and learning involved that is specific to firms and that may need to be promoted. Moreover, since there are no externalities involved in developing capabilities, and competitive advantages are given only by changing factor endowments, there can be no dynamic benefits in promoting the local base of technological capabilities. Since TNCs are an important mode of accessing foreign technologies and skills, therefore, no conditions should be put on their entry — their presence can only benefit local productivity and competitiveness.

The alternative approach to industrial development, based on the analysis of the micro-level process of capability building, offers quite different insights into the same phenomenon. It suggests that technology is not perfectly transferable, but has many 'tacit' elements that need the buyer to invest in developing new skills and technical and organisational information. Thus, the process of gaining technological competence cannot be instantaneous, costless or automatic, even if the technology is well diffused elsewhere. It is generally risky and unpredictable, and often itself has to be learnt (in the sense that firms may not even know what their deficiencies are or how to go about remedying them). The development of competitive capabilities may be costly and prolonged, depending on the complexity and scale of the technology. It usually involves interactions with other firms and institutions: apart from physical inputs, it calls for various new skills from the education system and training institutes, technical information and services, contract research facilities, interactions with equipment suppliers and consultants, standards bodies, and so on. The setting up of this dense network of co-operation needs the development of special skills. This constant and uncertain process of learning differs radically from the standard neoclassical model of firm development, and leads to different policy implications.

Industrial development is not just about starting new activities. As economies progress and mature, it involves *deepening* in any or all of four forms — technological upgrading of products and processes within industries, entry into more complex and demanding new activities, increasing local content, and mastering more complex technological tasks within industries (from those relevant to assembly to those needed for more value-added activity, adaptation, improvement, and finally design, development and innovation). *Each involves its own learning costs. These costs differ by activity, rising with the sophistication of the technology, the extent of linkages and the level of technological capabilities aimed at.* Progressive deepening is to some extent a natural part of industrial development, but it is not inevitable. Its pattern and incidence differ greatly, depending on the strategies pursued by the government.

The process of capability development may face various market failures. Free markets may not give correct signals to resource allocation in two main ways. First, the existence of learning costs and other capability development may distort allocation between simple and difficult activities. This is the classic case for *infant industry protection.* In the presence of learning costs, a latecomer to industry necessarily faces a disadvantage compared to those that have undergone the learning process. Given the unpredictability, lack of information and capital markets imperfections that are endemic to developing countries, exposure to full import competition can prevent entry into activities with relatively difficult technologies. Moreover, since learning costs differ between activities, interventions to ensure efficient resource allocation have to be selective rather than uniform. In simple activities the need for protection may be minimal, because the learning period is relatively brief, easy to get information on, and predictable. In complex activities, with large scales, advanced information and skill needs, wide linkages and intricate organisations, by contrast, the learning process could spread over years, even decades.[12] These may never be undertaken (unless there is a strong natural resource cost advantage) unless protection is given.

There is another argument for selectivity. Different activities have different externalities. Some have intense linkages with other activities and some activities have greater dynamic potential for creating new knowledge and technological advance than others. To the extent that private agents cannot take full account of such externalities and dynamic effects there is an argument for supporting activities selectively.

The second kind of form of market failure is more directly relevant to the present analysis of FDI: in resource allocation in the *deepening of capabilities*. Arrow (1962) noted long ago that a free market may fail to ensure optimal private investments in innovative activity because of imperfect appropriability of information and skills. While this was set in developed countries, a very similar argument applies to capability building, which has many of the investment aspects (risky and uncertain future payoff) of innovation. However, developing countries face an additional problem. Much of their investment is concerned with absorbing technologies that already exist overseas. It may be much easier to import foreign technologies fully 'packaged' — where the process is commercially proven, and the technology supplier provides the hard- and software, does the start-up, training and adaptation, and manages the operation and marketing — than to invest in developing further capabilities. Given the desirability of importing basic technical knowledge, and the universal need to create operational capabilities, there remains a further 'make-buy' choice in the creation of additional knowledge. The choice is affected by the mode of technology transfer, in particular between internalised and externalised modes.

7.4.3 TNCs and capability development

FDI in its classic form is the most 'internalised' form of technology transfer. While it is a relatively effective and low risk means of acquiring technology, and has in-built remedies to many of the market failures that affect technological mastery, these advantages themselves can affect the development of local technological capabilities. They may relieve the local firm of the need to invest in developing many kinds of skills, especially the more advanced ones of design and development. Innovative activity by TNCs tends to be concentrated in a few developed countries, because of the availability of special technical skills, large local markets, linkages with established suppliers and buyers, closeness to advanced science and technology institutions, and proximity to central decision making. The upgrading of capabilities in developing countries from production to innovation involves high learning costs which foreign investors tend to be unwilling to take.

However, the deepening of innovative capabilities is in the interests of countries that have reached a certain level of industrial development. The development should not be aimed at the creation of high-tech hothouses that are immensely costly and do not lead to competitive manufacturing activity. Nor should it seek to 'reinvent the wheel' in simple technologies. It should start with the import of technology that already exists and should be geared to achieving the next step of technological competence. The aim should by to allow local industries to absorb advanced import technologies,[13] lower the cost of technology import, develop its own products and processes, and better use local resources and linkages.

In fact, such investments do not only help local firms; they also help to attract higher value-added FDI. If local innovative capabilities are advanced, it is in the interests of TNCs to transfer more R&D activities to those countries (even though they would not invest in the first place to develop those capabilities). That innovative capabilities *can* be developed cost effectively is shown by the experience of the larger Asian NIEs (below). Their experience has shown that the dynamic benefits of developing local innovative capabilities are potentially very large, if done in an export-oriented framework where its benefits are exploited in international markets. The role of innovative capabilities is accepted widely as a source of comparative advantage in advanced industrial countries — what is not appreciated is that a similar capability has to be acquired by developing countries that are approaching the frontiers of 'easy' technologies and have to move into more complex activities.

The risk of market failure here is that a *passive dependence on TNCs* for technology can stultify the process of industrial deepening, since most innovative activities will continue to be performed overseas and the relevant skills and institutions will not develop locally (Lall, 1985). This will curtail the move of the host economy into higher value-added activities, deprive it of the externalities generated by local innovation, and subject its export activities to the global strategies of TNCs rather than to its own evolving competitiveness. To ensure a more desirable allocation of technological effort, therefore, it may be necessary to intervene selectively. If it is accepted that *some* interventions are needed to speed up technological development, then TNCs cannot be the 'new custodians of development' in any straightforward way. *Market failures call for the custodian role to be fulfilled by the government.*

However, this does not amount to a general argument for restricting FDI. There are numerous ways in which local technological capabilities can be deepened, some of which may be compatible with considerable reliance on FDI. In general, we can distinguish two broad strategies for intervention to promote technological deepening. The first accepts the presence of TNCs but seeks to deepen local technological activity within the foreign production framework, the second to induce local firms to invest in advanced forms of technological capabilities:

• Continue to attract FDI to the maximum extent possible, but induce TNCs, by a mixture of incentives, rules and negotiations as well as investments in local skills and institutions, to enter activities with more complex technologies, upgrade local technological capabilities within given activities, establish closer linkages with local technology institutions and set up local R&D units.
• Restrict technology import in 'internalised' forms and promote those in 'externalised' forms (for instance, by licensing, capital goods imports, turnkey plants, subcontracting or majority local ventures). Here local firms retain control and invest in deepening and extending their technological capabilities, while continuing to draw upon imported technologies and equipment.

It should be noted, however, that local control by itself does not ensure that innovative capabilities will be developed, since local firms may choose to remain passively dependent on continued purchases of foreign technology and skills. In fact, if local firms are worse endowed with technical skills and managerial capabilities, and are more risk averse, they may (and often do) develop lower levels of technological capabilities than foreign counterparts. The development of deeper local capabilities requires complementary interventions to ensure that incentives exist to invest in such risky activity, that the right sorts of skills and information are available to firms, and that the capital market is able and willing to finance the process (or else local firms are promoted to a large enough size that enables them to internalise capital and other relevant markets).

If, however, such supporting interventions can be mounted, are there any reasons to prefer the second strategy over the first? There may well be. Local enterprises are generally likely to be more amenable to pressures from a host government than TNCs that have many other potential sites for locating their affiliates. Local firms may be less resistant to technological investments because they have no sunk costs of R&D facilities elsewhere, and are more likely to use local suppliers and establish linkages with local science institutions than TNCs. Once R&D activity is undertaken, local firms are likely to generate greater externalities for the developing economy than a TNC that could internalise the results of the research and deploy it elsewhere.

Experience shows that in most developing countries local firms tend to perform more R&D than foreign counterparts. Moreover, foreign affiliates may be present in developing countries for decades without investing in local design and development capabilities. The contrast, for instance, between the large Latin American economies, with their long history of relatively passive dependence on TNCs, and the larger Asian NIEs is instructive. Mexico, with an industrial sector of roughly the same value-added as Korea, spends only about 0.03% of GDP on R&D by productive enterprises as compared to 1.7% by the latter. Mexico has a high level of dependence on foreign firms in most high technology activities, while Korea has a relatively marginal presence of TNCs (below) (Lall and Najmabadi, 1993). The export structure and performance of Mexico is not comparable to that of Korea, in terms of the sophistication of the products or the rates of growth.

There is thus *even stronger* reason to argue that TNCs cannot be the 'new custodians of development". Even with selective interventions, there may be good reason to discriminate selectively in favour of local firms to promote technological development. The key word of course is 'selectively'. Indiscriminate policies to promote local firms, especially in protected import-substitution regimes, have proved to be enormously costly and inefficient in the recent past. Interventions have to be mounted carefully, and in a few cases at a time, to address specific market failures. Selective intervention is best conducted in an export-oriented setting which provides strong incentives to invest in local capabilities. The protection of local firms has to be placed in the context of the growth of international integration of production, where there may be no effective local substitutes for TNCs in a number of activities. Such protection has to be matched by interventions that lead to technological investments rather than sloth and waste.

Demanding though these requirements of intervention are, there is good evidence that they can be fulfilled by developing countries. The next section looks at some such evidence.

7.4.4 Asian NIEs and TNCs

While the details of the East Asian development experience cannot be recounted here, it is worth summarising some features of their FDI policies. The high growth economies of East Asia may be divided into four broad categories as far as FDI strategies are concerned. The categorisation is crude and ignores many important distinctions between the strategies of the individual countries; nevertheless, it is useful for present purposes. The four groups are:

- Those that followed passive open door policies on TNCs and did not intervene to promote industrial development in other ways (e.g. Hong Kong),
- Those that pursued active industrial policies for certain sectors and promoted local enterprises in certain activities, but adopted effectively open-door, non-interventionist policies in some export-oriented sectors (e.g. Thailand, Malaysia),
- Those that actively sought heavy TNC participation in manufacturing, but intervened selectively to guide investors in directions and technological activity thought desirable for industrial upgrading (e.g. Singapore), and
- Those that selectively restricted FDI and sought to maximise reliance on externalised forms of technology transfer in the context of a comprehensive set of industrial policies to deepen the manufacturing sector, promote local linkages and increase local innovative capabilities (e.g. Korea and Taiwan, and earlier Japan). These industrial policies encompassed interventions in trade, finance, skills, technology and institution building, with strongly selective aspects to practically all interventions.

Table 7.2 shows the share of FDI in gross domestic capital formation in these selected countries. It also shows R&D by productive enterprises as a percentage of GDP in a recent year. It shows, in very broad terms, that the countries that developed the most diverse, complex and technologically dynamic industrial sectors (Korea, Taiwan and Japan) had the least reliance on FDI. There was evidently a causal connection between industrial policy, selective restrictions of foreign investment, the pursuit of technological deepening and export-orientation that allowed these countries to achieve historically unprecedented rates of industrial growth. Certainly, their industrial strategies were aimed at the development of indigenous capabilities, and certainly selectivity on FDI was one important aspect of their strategies. These are issues on which the conventional neoclassical interpretation of the East Asian 'miracle' (World Bank, 1993) has little to say (Lall, 1994.a).

Table 7.2 FDI as % of domestic investment and R&D as % of GDP

Country	FDI % GDI 1981–85	FDI % GDI 1986–91	R&D by productive enterprises % GDP
Hong Kong	10.7	11.4	0.3 (est)
Thailand	3.1	6.3	0.03
Malaysia	10.8	9.7	0.1
Singapore	17.4	29.4	0.2
Korea	0.5	1.1	1.3
Taiwan	1.5	3.5	0.6
Japan	0.1	0.1	1.9

Sources: UNCTAD (1993), Lall (1992), ADB (1994)

The above interpretation of these figures is clearly oversimplified, and a number of comments may be in order to amplify on it:

First, the most liberal regime, **Hong Kong**, was able to attract substantial amounts of FDI, and at the same time have a dynamic indigenous industrial class that was very successful on export markets. Hong Kong is, however, a very special case, by virtue of its location, long entrepôt tradition, presence of large and highly developed British trading and financial companies, and the influx of entrepreneurs and trained engineers/technicians from mainland China after the communist take-over. This allowed it to launch into export-oriented light manufacturing — the relatively brief learning period for garment manufacturing had been undergone already in China, and for the other activities (toys, watches and the like)could be financed locally.

However, because of the essentially *laissez* faire policies pursued, Hong Kong's industrialisation shows special features. The colony started *and stayed with* light labour-intensive manufacturing industry, though within this there was considerable upgrading. Hong Kong's success was based on an impressive development of operational and marketing capabilities, but there was little industrial deepening and diversification because of the lack of promotion of more demanding complex technological learning. There was some 'natural' progression up the ladder of industrial complexity, but it was relatively limited in relation to other NIEs. As wages and land costs rose, the colony had to relocate its manufacturing to other countries, mainly mainland China, and suffered a significant loss of industrial activity at home (over 1986–92 it lost about 35% of its manufacturing employment, and the process is continuing[14]). The growth of its manufactured exports has slowed down considerably, and may even have gone into decline in 1993–94. Its impressive overseas investment performance, especially in China, was a reflection of its advanced entrepreneurial and limited technological capabilities rather than of broad industrial strengths (Lall, 1993a). At the same time, the lack of a strong technology base is worrying the government, and it is now launching initiatives like the Hong Kong Industrial Technology Centre to selectively promote local high-tech companies.[15]

Second, **Malaysia** has been able to develop an impressive array of high-technology exports driven almost entirely by FDI (ADB, 1994). It was fortunate in targeting and attracting electronics assembly when the burst of labour-intensive activity started in developing countries. Its excellent infrastructure, stable and open economy, low wages and use of English made it an ideal investment site, an advantage that seemed to grow over time despite the fact that it imposed various equity sharing and other conditions on investors that were not wholly export-oriented. It benefited greatly from its location in a hub of dynamic growth, much of it driven by strategic industrial policy in the larger countries like Japan, Korea and Taiwan. As technologies progressed and wages rose, TNCs responded by automating their facilities in Malaysia and diversifying; other assembly operations were attracted, and today the country has some $34 billion of manufactures exports. At the same time, Malaysia pursued active industrial policies in other activities, setting up public enterprises, promoting *bumiputra* ownership, helping small and medium firms and upgrading resource-based activities. To a large extent, however, these activities remained detached from the TNC sphere of manufacturing for export.

Has this dependence on FDI hampered Malaysian growth? The evidence suggests not. However, the Malaysian government is worried about its ability to sustain the growth of its exports in the face of rising wages. The pattern of industrial development has been skewed towards electronics and electrical industries, which remain assembly operations (though now fairly capital rather than labour intensive) with low local linkages, little local design and development activity and no independent marketing capabilities. The scarcity of local technical skills is constraining further upgrading. The paucity of indigenous suppliers and technology support makes local R&D uneconomic for TNCs. As noted earlier, FDI approvals last year dropped by 60%; over a longer period, FDI in high technology activities has been stagnating. The government has ambitious technology development plans, drawing very much on the Korean model. It is also launching selective policies towards TNCs to induce technological deepening and greater local content. However, its past strategies and current phase of liberalisation restrict any move into a Korean style of industrial policy. Clearly, FDI in a latecomer can do wonders for export performance and manufacturing output if certain conditions are met, but its impact on local technological capabilities remains weak. The conditions offered by Malaysia are unusual, and practically no other country (including its neighbours) has been able to reproduce them. The Thai export drive, for instance, is far more concentrated in low-technology assembly activity, and Indonesia even more so.

Third, **Singapore** has the highest reliance of almost any country on TNCs, and has done extremely well from it. Its government has been very interventionist, but the form of interventionism has been very different from Korea's. The economy started with a base of capabilities in *entrepôt* trading, ship servicing and petroleum refining. After a brief period of import substitution, it moved into export-oriented industrialisation, based overwhelmingly on investment by multinational companies. Unlike Hong Kong, there was a weak tradition of local entrepreneurship, and there was no influx of technical and entrepreneurial know-how from China. There was a decade or so of light industrial activity (garment and semiconductor assembly), after which the Singaporean government acted firmly to upgrade the industrial structure. It intervened in foreign investments to guide TNCs to higher value-added activities, and in education to create the specific high-level technical skills that would be needed.[16] The government also set up a number of public enterprises to enter a number of activities that it considered would be in the country's future comparative advantage (including, most recently, an investment push into China); the public sector in Singapore accounts for a substantial proportion of GDP.

Specific areas of both manufacturing and services (like banking, freighting and aircraft servicing) were selected for promotion by the Singaporean government, but the policy instruments used did not include trade protection. Instead, they comprised a range of incentives and pressures that guided the allocation of foreign and local resources and lowered the cost of entry into difficult activities (by providing the requisite skills and infrastructure). Manufacturing activity was taken into highly specialised processes and products, but there was no attempt to deliberately increase local content. Such specialisation, along with the heavy reliance on foreign investments for technology and skill transfer, greatly reduced the need for indigenous technological investments (as compared, say, to Korea). Thus, while selective interventions led Singapore's industry into sophisticated producer and consumer electronics, precision instruments, optics and so on, the technological depth of the enterprises located there remained comparatively low. Some design and development activity did develop over time, but this was again with considerable urging and support from the government (Hobday, 1994).

The lessons of Singapore, to the extent that an economy with 3 million people is relevant to most of the developing world, are twofold. First, FDI can take a small economy a long way if it is carefully selected and guided, supplied with superlative infrastructure and a disciplined and trained workforce, and given a competitive and stable investment environment. Second, it is not necessary to offer import protection to technologically complex activities if the main sources of operational and other technologies remain foreign, production is integrated with that in foreign countries (rather than with local suppliers) and is concentrated on some stages of production. This strategy requires both functional and selective interventions by the government: the contrasting experiences of Singapore and Hong Kong with respect to the deepening of industrial activity illustrate this clearly.

Finally, the cases of **Korea** and **Taiwan** are too well known now to need much description here.[17] It only needs to be reiterated that the role of FDI was secondary to that of technology import in other forms, that the export drive was led by local firms, and that a series of interventions (integrated across product and factor markets) allowed local firms to develop impressive technological capabilities. Korea went much further in developing advanced innovative capabilities than Taiwan, though perhaps at the cost of a more concentrated industrial structure and a worsening of income distribution. To achieve this compressed entry into heavy industry, its interventions also had to be more detailed and pervasive. Unlike Taiwan, therefore, Korea had to promote the growth of giant conglomerates (to internalise poorly functioning markets and bear the risk of going into demanding activities at world levels of efficiency), though the former tried to enter heavy industry with public sector enterprises. Both invested heavily in higher education and technical training, and both set up a range of technology support institutions. Strong incentives (including subsidies and cheap credit) were given to promote local R&D and to use local research institutes. The state took a strong lead in targeting sectors for technology development, and both countries have selected around ten to twelve activities for investment to promote their future comparative advantage.

For present purposes, the most important point about their experience, and that of Japan, is that while TNCs were an important input into their industrialisation, they were used by the respective governments in furthering the acquisition of technology and the development of local innovative capabilities. The externalities generated by these capabilities were captured by local firms and used to dynamise the countries' comparative advantage. The internalised markets of TNCs were not, in other words, allowed to weaken the deficient factor markets of the host economies, but were tapped in such a way that local capabilities were strengthened. As their capabilities grew, FDI was allowed to play a larger role, but it never became the 'custodian of development'.

This paper takes a somewhat stronger, but essentially not very different, position on the effects of TNCs on domestic technological development than Helleiner does in his survey. As noted at the start, Helleiner finds that the issue of the best conditions for domestic learning is still unresolved and the empirical evidence on developing countries technological development difficult to assess. In this he is correct, but my own work on the details of capability acquisition suggests that we can still attach a question mark to the title of this paper. Of course ambiguities remain, and many other factors intervene in the causal chain between investment inflows and domestic technological activity.

7.4.5 Some implications of not intervening

The experience of these larger NIEs also shows that *it is possible for developing country governments to design and implement selective interventions* in trade, investment and domestic resource allocation so as to accelerate growth and deepen local capabilities. Many neoclassical interpretations of development policy seem to suggest that while in theory interventions could improve upon markets, this is impossible in practice. The information, skill and neutrality requirements are thought to be beyond the capabilities of any government, so much so that it seems logically impossible for selective interventions to ever succeed. The evidence does not support such a sweeping or pessimistic conclusion. 'Efficient intervention' is not an oxymoron.

However, it is true that the conditions under which governments can exercise efficient intervention are not often found in developing countries. The risk of government failure is so great in some cases that it may be better to suffer the consequences of market failure than to indulge in selectivity. In such cases the government should confine itself to 'market friendly' interventions and entrust the custodian role to free markets in trade and investment. However, government capabilities are also not static or given in perpetuity; they can be improved and disciplined. There are, moreover, various levels of selectivity in intervention. The Korean strategy was at one extreme in selectivity, and its high rewards accompanied high degrees of risk. Taiwan's was far less detailed in its selectivity, and its potential costs were also lower. It should be possible to gear the strategy to minimise the cost of failure. It is crucial to note in this context that *not* intervening also carries costs. There are many countries outside of South East Asia that have pursued liberal trade and investment policies without achieving the kind of industrial and technological success of the East Asian NIEs.

Let us take an interesting example. **Chile** is often cited as a case of a Latin American 'tiger', with its success traceable to free market and open door policies. The data on its modest rates of industrial and manufactured export growth suggest, however, that the longest history of liberalisation in the developing world has not produced a NIE in the Asian mould. Chile's annual rates of growth of manufacturing production and total commodity exports were 0.6% and 7.9% respectively during 1965—80 (liberalisation started in the middle of this period, in 1973), and 3.6% and 5.2% during 1980—90. This may be better than many other Latin American countries in the latter period, but it is rather modest by the standards of most Asian countries, even those with massive interventions.[18] The total value of Chile's *manufactured* exports came to $1.3 billion in 1992,[19] compared to $70.0 billion for Taiwan in the same year — Chile's population was two-thirds of Taiwan's, so in terms of size the two are roughly comparable. On a *per capita* basis, Chile's manufactured exports were $96, as compared to $3,500 for Taiwan. Though Chile received significant FDI (6.3% of domestic investment during 1981—85 and 5.7% during 1986—91), especially during privatisation, much of the inflow went into resource-based and service activities. It did not 'do a Malaysia' in terms of using FDI to dynamise its industrial and export sector despite far more open policies and high levels of human and natural resources.

During 1980—87, by which time liberal policies may be taken to be well established in Chile, the rate of growth of its manufactured exports was 3.3% per annum, compared to 13% for Taiwan and over 20% for Malaysia. Unlike Taiwan and other East Asian NIEs, whose export dynamism was driven by diversification into non-resource based activities and encompassed increasingly skill- and technology-intensive activities, Chile's export growth in manufactures was based largely on the further processing of natural resources. Because of this, the skill and technology content of its exports diminished over time.[20] Thus, the share of high wage products in total manufactured exports (an indicator of skill-intensity) fell over the period 1966—86, as did the share of products intensive in the use of technical and engineering manpower (an index of technological intensity). In Taiwan and Malaysia, by contrast, these shares rose sharply.

This is not to say that there was no dynamism in Chilean exports. In agro-based activities Chile introduced new products and developed new markets. Chile had a resource advantage in its traditionally strong agricultural sector (aided by the dovetailing of its seasons into those of countries in the northern hemisphere), a good base of skills in these activities, and government support for research into biotechnology — this was, interestingly, the only intervention in the export related field undertaken by the Chilean government until recently. The base of agricultural exports and capabilities provided a cushion for Chilean enterprises to invest in technological effort related to the further processing of those exports. Thus, much of its manufactured export growth was based on its natural resource base, with its learning process stimulated by export prospects and a degree of natural protection. The capability approach still provides a good explanation of the pattern of export growth that resulted under liberal policies, but it gives additional insights. The main insight is that, despite two decades of stringent neoclassical policies to 'free up' its competitiveness from the shackles of government intervention, Chile failed to transform its manufacturing sector into an engine of export growth.

7.5 CONCLUSIONS

Relations between TNCs and developing countries have evolved a great deal in recent years, and much of the heat has gone out of the debate — in fact, there is very little debate left. The inexorable spread of international production, the shrinking of economic space, the growth of overseas investment by developing countries themselves, and changing perceptions of the role of markets and governments, have all made the Third World a much more congenial place for TNCs. Much of this change is desirable and inevitable. Past development strategies based on nationalism and massive interventions do not inspire any confidence.

There is, however, a grave risk that the pendulum will swing too far in favour of free market policies and against the legitimate and necessary role of governments. As long as the development process is confronted with widespread market failures, there are good reasons (theoretical and empirical) to believe that careful selective and functional interventions can speed up the process. This applies to FDI as well as to other international economic relations.

The main risk, and it is a very serious one, is of government failure. If institutional changes are needed, it is in the sphere of *strengthening government capabilities* to mount economically desirable interventions rather than in setting up new international bodies to regulate TNCs. That this can be done is not in doubt. The World Bank's East Asian 'miracle' study, while hemmed in by its ideological aversion to interventions, has some useful lessons to draw from the effective interventions undertaken by governments there. Most of these are fairly evident, some to the point of banality — pay better salaries, give better training and education, insulate from political processes. Others are more interesting: intervene in the context of export orientation and provide favours only in return for performance (exports), set up institutional mechanisms for regular and intense consultation between officials and business, and collect and analyse information on relevant economic developments. Even many of the obvious measures are not undertaken by many developing country governments.

If they are, some careful interventions can be mounted to promote the development of local enterprise and capabilities within a fairly welcoming regime for FDI. Helleiner is right to point to the need for further investigation of this complex subject, and to conclude that 'the actual effects of market concentration and internalisation of international trade are still only imperfectly understood'. It is important that we do not allow the assumption that there is nothing further to study to pass unchallenged.

NOTES AND REFERENCES

1. One of the more important among these is the World Bank's new (1993) study of the East Asian economic 'miracle'
2. These arguments are further developed in Lall (1992, 1993.b, 1994).
3. The developed world is defined in conventional terms here, excluding NIEs like Hong Kong and Singapore as well as Mexico (which has just joined the OECD).
4. Cited in the Singapore newspaper *The Straits Times*, April 13, 1994, "Asean falling behind China and India in race for investments".
5. For a detailed analysis of technological capabilities in Ghana, the country with the longest history of structural adjustment in sub-Saharan Africa, and its failure to achieve competitive production and attract DFI, see Lall *et al.* (1994).
6. See Oman (1984) for an analysis of the nature and growth of "new" forms of international investment.
7. One of the more interesting ones is the growth of software sourcing by a number of computer firms and users in Bangalore, India. Many of these facilities are linked by dedicated satellite connections and can exchange data in real time with centres in the USA and Europe.
8. The analysis of transfer pricing is surveyed in Plasschaert (1994).
9. Lall *et al.* (1983). Also see the comprehensive and perceptive analysis of Third World TNCs by Tolentino (1993).
10. Singapore is also making a determined effort to boost its investments in China. As usual in Singapore, the lead is coming from the government, which is pulling together private firms in a bid to develop one area on China into a mini-Singapore.

11. This role has been very different from the non-economic interventions carried out in classic import-substitution regimes, with strong nationalist overtones and with a disregard of market forces and market failures. Not surprisingly, such interventions had poor economic outcomes.
12. See Jacobsson (1993) on the heavy engineering industry in Korea.
13. One of the main functions of R&D, in developed countries as well as elsewhere, is simply to keep up with the technology frontier and to assimilate advances in complex activities (Cohen and Levinthal, 1989).
14. *Financial Times,* London, 4 May, 1993, "Survey of Hong Kong", p. 6. A recent article in the *Far Eastern Economic Review* (26 May, 1994, p. 68) shows that manufacturing employment declined from 45% to 23% of the total in 1980-92.
15. *Far Eastern Economic Review*, May 26, 1994, p. 69.
16. When the local skill base was unable to cope the government allowed a controlled import of skilled manpower.
17. For a summary description see Lall (1994.b).
18. For instance, India's rates of growth in these periods were 4.5% and 6.7% for manufacturing and 3.7% and 7.4% for exports. Data for the NIEs were given earlier.
19. Data from various *World Development Reports.*
20. For a full analysis of Chile's export performance, see Pietrobelli (1994).

BIBLIOGRAPHY

ADB (1994) *Malaysia's Export Performance and Its Sustainability*, Manila: Asian Development Bank, Draft.

ARROW, K. (1962) 'Economic Welfare and the Allocation on Resources for Innovation', in R. Nelson (ed.), *The Rate and Direction of Innovative Activity* (Princeton: Princeton University Press,).

COHEN, W. M. and D.A. LEVINTHAL (1989) 'Innovation and Learning: The Two Faces of R&D', *Economic Journal,* 99:4, pp. 569—96.

DUNNING, J. H. (1988) *Explaining International Production*, London: Unwin Hyman.

HELLEINER, G. K. (1973) 'Manufactured Exports from Less Developed Countries and Multinational Firms', *Economic Journal*, 83: 21-47.

HELLEINER, G. K. (1981) *Intra-Firm Trade and the Developing Countries*, London: Macmillan.

HELLEINER, G. K. (1989) 'Transnational Corporations and Direct Foreign Investment', in H. B. Chenery and T. N. Srinivasan (eds), *Handbook of Development Economics*, Amsterdam: Elsevier Science Publishers.

HOBDAY, M. G. (1994) 'Technological Learning in Singapore: A Test Case of Leapfrogging', *Journal of Development Studies* (forthcoming).

LALL, S. (1985) 'Multinationals and Technology Development in Host Countries', in S. Lall, *Multinationals, Technology and Exports*, London:

Macmillan.

LALL, S. (1992a) 'Technological Capabilities and Industrialization', *World Development*, February, 20(2): 165—86.

LALL, S. (1992b) 'Structural Problems of African Industry', in F. Stewart, S. Lall and S. Wangwe (eds), *Alternative Development Strategies in Sub-Saharan Africa*, London: Macmillan.

LALL, S. (1993a) 'Foreign Direct Investment in South Asia', *Asian Development Review*, 11(1), pp. 103-119.

LALL, S. (1993b) 'Understanding Technology Development', *Development and Change*, 24(4), pp. 719-753.

LALL, S. (1994a) 'The East Asian Miracle', Study: Does The Bell Toll for Industrial Strategy?', *World Development*, 22(4): 1-10.

LALL, S. (1994b) 'Industrial Adaptation and Technological Capabilities in Developing Countries', in T. Killick (ed), *The Nature, Significance and Determinants of Flexibility in National Economies*, London: Routledge, 1994.

LALL, S. (forthcoming), 'Transnational Corporations and Economic Development', in J. H. Dunning and Karl Sauvant (eds), *Transnational Corporations and World Development*, London: Routledge.

LALL, S. *et al.* (1983) *The New Multinationals: The Spread of Third World Enterprises*, Chichester: J. Wiley.

LALL, S. and F. NAJMABADI (1993) *Bank Lending for Industrial Technology Development*, World Bank, Operations Evaluation Department, Report no 12138.

LALL, S., G.B. NAVARETTI, S. TEITEL and G. WIGNARAJA (1994), *Technology and Enterprise Development: Ghana under Structural Adjustment*, London: Macmillan.

OMAN, C. (1984) *New Forms of International Investment in Developing Countries*, Paris: OECD.

PIETROBELLI, C. (1994) 'Technological Capability and Export Diversification in a Developing County: The Case of Chile Since 1974', D.Phil. thesis, Oxford.

PLASSCHAERT, S. (ed.) (1994) *Transnational Corporations: Transfer Pricing and Taxation*, London: Routledge, United Nations Library on Transnational Corporations, vol. 14.

PLASSCHAERT, S. (ed.) (1989) *Multinational Enterprises and National Policies*, Rome: Herder.

TOLENTINO, P. E. E. (1993) *Technological Innovation and Third World Multinationals*, London: Routledge.

UNCTAD, Division on Transnational Corporations and Investment (1994) *World Investment Report 1994*, United Nations.

UNCTAD, Programme on Transnational Corporations (1993) *World Investment Report 1993*, United Nations.

WESTPHAL, L. E., Y.W. RHEE and G. PURSELL (1979) 'Foreign Influences on Korea's Industrial Development', *Oxford Bulletin of Economics and Statistics*, 41(4): 359-388.

World Bank (1993) *The East Asian Miracle: Economic Growth and Public Policy*, New York: Oxford University Press.

8 Foreign Equity Joint Ventures in China: Interactions between Government Policies and Multinational Investment Strategies

Danny Van Den Bulcke
and Haiyan Zhang

8.1 INTRODUCTION

The growing interdependence between national economies and the worldwide globalization of business activities during the last two decades have created serious limits to the self-sufficient economic development options of individual countries. While the proportion of the national economy which is subject to foreign influence has grown for most nations, external policy considerations have become increasingly important in national economic development programmes (Stopford and Strange, 1991). This is especially true for an emerging market economy such as China. The frequent adaptations of Chinese foreign direct investment (FDI) policy since the end of the 1970s and the growing importance of multinational enterprises (MNEs) in the Chinese economy provide an interesting example of the dynamic interaction between national policy measures and MNE strategies against the background of the globalization of the world economy.

According to the World Investment Report (UNCTAD, 1994:68), already in 1993 China had become the second largest host country in the world after the United States and the primary destination of FDI of all developing countries. Since 1979, when it opened up to world investment, China approved about 175 thousand FDI projects, with a total contracted foreign commitment of more than US$224 billion, and a current value which reached US$63.7 billion[1]. The economic impact of FDI on China's development has become more and more evident. In 1993 the tax contributions of about 67 thousand operational foreign affiliates amounted to US$6.56 billion, while their export reached US$25 billion or 28% of the total Chinese export activity[2]. The employment of these foreign enterprises was estimated at about 6 million people, or 4.05% of the total urban workforce of China (Zhan, 1993).

This chapter examines the main changes of Chinese FDI policy since the end of the 1970s and their effect on the patterns of multinational investment in China. The first section provides some theoretical background to assess the dynamic interactions between on the one hand the Country Specific Advantages (CSAs) and the FDI policy of the host government and on the other hand the Firm Specific Advantages (FSAs) and strategic positioning of MNEs. The second part presents a chronological overview of the evolution of Chinese FDI policy in the context of Chinese economic reform and probes for its significance with respect to FDI. The third section examines some of the major characteristics of FDI in China, especially with regard to the sino-foreign Equity Joint Ventures (EJVs), which — with about 44% of the total contracted value and 57% of current value of Chinese inward FDI at the end of 1992 — are the dominant form of FDI operations in China[3].

The data base for this study covers 3,461 EJVs, which were registered between 1979-1990 by the Ministry of Foreign Trade and Economic Cooperation (MOFTEC) in its *Almanac of China's foreign economic relations and trade*[4]. These EJVs represent about one fifth of all EJV projects approved in China during this twelve year period and about one third in terms of the foreign equity contribution. Although the criteria, used by MOFTEC to select these companies were not explicitly mentioned, all important and 'promoted' EJV projects in China are included. This extensive sample is therefore assumed to capture the evolution and behaviour of foreign EJVs under the FDI policy of the Chinese government. The data set provides information about: the country of origin of the investor, the type of business activity, the size of the project in terms of total investment, the foreign equity contribution, the ownership structure and the location and duration of the EJVs. The statistical methods used are, on the one hand the oneway analysis of variance, which shows differences of EJVs in term of project size, foreign equity contribution, ownership structure and EJV's duration, and on the other hand, the crosstabulation analysis, which examines the patterns of EJVs according to their country of origin, geographic location, sectorial distribution and period of establishment.

8.2 BACKGROUND

Today, global economic interdependence is no longer mainly based on foreign trade as it was in the 1950s and 1960s, but relies increasingly on the multinationalisation of production activities. As FDI has to some extent overtaken trade as the driving force in international economic relations, the nature of the external policies and the appropriate measures of the national governments are also changing (UNCTC, 1993:113). The FDI policy of the host country is increasingly influenced by the globalization and strategic positioning of MNEs. Three recent trends are of special relevance. First, national governments tend to enhance their capabilities and competitiveness by integrating the FDI policy into their so called 'macro-organizational strategy' (Dunning, 1992, Ostry, 1992), rather than to set up certain 'interventionist' tax and tariff measures. Secondly, more and more MNEs regard their overseas subsidiaries as a part of their cross-border value-added chain, rather than country-by-country stand-alone operations (Yip, 1989, Plasschaert and Van Den Bulcke, 1991, UNCTC, 1993). Thirdly, both the evolution of MNEs from stand-alone operations to global strategic activities and the integration of the FDI policy into the national macro-organizational strategy by the national government result in 'deep' linkages between the host country and MNEs (Streeten, 1992, UNCTC, 1993).

The FDI regulatory measures, which until recently were mainly used by developing host countries, were typically related to different aspects of the national economic and organizational system, such as ownership structure, resource allocation, tax and tariff incentives, foreign exchange control, pricing policy, performance requirements, sectorial preferences, administrative procedures, etc. (Van Den Bulcke, 1988, Contractor, 1990). These measures varied over time in order to monitor foreign investment patterns on the basis of the national development strategy. In an early stage the national government often regulated FDI within certain specific targets — such as employment creation, import substitution and/or export promotion — without changing its global development strategy as such. The incentives of FDI policy at this stage consisted e.g. of the setting-up of export processing zones, the granting of tariff protection, fiscal incentives and specific political interventions, while the control over the activities of the MNEs was generally based on administrative regulations and procedures, such as e.g. specifications about location and limits on the degree of foreign ownership, according to whether one wanted to stimulate or restrict FDI. The CSAs under this 'interventionist' policy for MNEs mainly consist of the availability of, e.g. local natural resources including unskilled labour, low cost land, abundant raw materials, etc.

At a later stage, the FDI policy of the host country often becomes more integrated into a 'sound macroeconomic policy' and a 'credible national development strategy' (UNCTAD, 1994:217). As a result, the national government will typically extend its role, from the provision to MNEs of natural factor endowments as in the first stage, to the enhancement of the created assets, the establishment and maintaining of an efficient market mechanism and the development of linkages between domestic and foreign firms. The capabilities of the existing physical and human resources will later be upgraded by investments in infrastructure, education, training, health care, etc., and as they will be allocated in a more performing market they will be used in a more optimal way (UNCTC, 1993:217). The switch from a 'limited' to a 'global' FDI policy will be greatly determined on the one hand by the positive evaluation of FDI by the host government and on the other hand by the pressures from MNEs to provide or improve specific local endowments. Consequently, the attractiveness of the host country for FDI will be upgraded by a number of measures to structurally 'integrate' the subsidiaries in the host country into global economic development options.

The foreign investment patterns of MNEs may be substantially affected by the changes of the FDI policy and the CSAs of the host country. At the early stage, MNEs tend to follow the specific policy targets of the host countries and to rely for their activities on the country-specific locational factors (e.g. natural resources and market potential). With the upgrading of the local market efficiency, MNEs tend to reinforce the upstream and downstream integration with the local market and to engage into more technology and organizational intensive operations. The relationship between the host government and MNEs becomes therefore more bargaining oriented, i.e. the growth of cross border integrated production and international investment networks leads to increased pressure from MNEs on the host government to reduce the transaction barriers and to provide a market efficient environment for their global operations. Of course, the investment patterns of MNEs are first of all determined by the FSAs and the changing strategic options of the parent companies. MNEs from countries which are at various stages of economic development and technological capabilities are also at different levels in the investment development path (Dunning, 1986, 1993) and the internationalization process. Next to the initial FSAs of MNEs and the 'country of origin effects', the organizational learning and corporate self-renewal of foreign subsidiaries influence the changing patterns of MNEs (Cantwell, 1989, Zander and Sölvell, 1992, Heldlund, 1992). Both the initial competitive position of the parent company and its previous experience in the host country are therefore expected to influence the investment behaviour and specific features of their overseas operations and to determine their bargaining position vis-à-vis the host government.

8.3 OVERVIEW OF CHINESE FOREIGN DIRECT INVESTMENT POLICY

Since the Chinese government opened its economy to foreign direct investment in 1979, a set of FDI regulatory measures were gradually introduced in its global economic reform and development programme. The process of liberalisation and upgrading of locational resources, the 'marketization'[5] of resource allocation, the building-up of a legal system geared to market transactions, the decentralisation of macro-economic management, the liberalization of ownership control and the introduction of performance requirements were all major changes which affected the investment pattern of MNEs both in terms of space and time and are documented in Table 8.1. Next to the government's FDI policies and decisions, this table indicates the main effects on the MNEs as well as their responses.

Geographical extension: The gradual opening up of specific locations to foreign investors, on the basis of preferential tax and tariff measures, was quite characteristic of the Chinese 'guided FDI scenario'. The first major step by the Chinese government was to establish four Special Economic Zones (SEZs) in two coastal provinces in 1980. The specific locational advantages of these zones were mainly related to their proximity to Hong Kong and the low labour costs which permitted firms from the Asian Newly Industrializing Economies

Table 8.1 Chronological overview of China's decisions and policies related to FDI and responses of MNEs (1979-1995)

Period	Government decisions and policies about FDI	Main effects on FDI and responses of MNEs
1979–82	• Abolishment of FDI prohibition by the introduction of Joint Venture Law, Civil Procedure Law, Joint Venture Income Tax Law, etc • Establishment of 4 Special Economic Zones (SEZs) • Incentives and regulatory measures of FDI dominated by the bureaucratic control mechanism	• Low cost labour seeking investment with export processing activities • Limited integration with domestic market (location mainly in the SEZs) • Limited resources and management commitment • Preference for contractual JVs and short term projects • 'Testing' investment by Western firms (strategic positioning)
1983–85	• Improvement of industrial infrastructure and better access to domestic market by opening up of 14 coastal cities • Integration of local labour intensive industries into export processing operations by opening up of 3 River Deltas • Introduction of reform measures in urban areas (fiscal, banking, pricing, local economic management, enterprise management) • Setting-up of preliminary legal infrastructure for market transactions (Contract law and patent law)	• Growth of market seeking investment • Introduction of more human resource intensive technology • More linkages with local market as result of increasing capabilities of local sourcing for export processing manufacture and involvement of local partners for acquiring local market knowledge in establishing EJVs
1986–88	• New regulatory measures (22 regulations) with additional incentives for priority FDI projects (export, import substitution and high-tech) • Introduction of performance requirements (export share, product specifics and technological level) • 'Marketization' of resource allocation (foreign exchange-SWAP markets, raw materials, labour) • Increasing liberalization of market resources (supply and distribution network)	• Increase of bargaining power of Western MNEs based on relatively high level of technology and new products • Increase of large scale export processing manufacturing industries • Decrease of short term FDI projects (in service sectors)

Period	Government decisions and policies about FDI	Main effects on FDI and responses of MNEs
1989–91	• Political crisis (aftermath of Tiananmen) and introduction of an 'rectification programme' to control the economic overheating and inflation • Neither restrictive nor significant incentive measures for FDI in the updated EJV Law in 1990 • Specific administrative arrangements for foreign investors to improve investment climate • Increasing support from bureaucracy for local market oriented foreign enterprises ('isolated' market)	• Reduction of confidence of foreign (especially Western) investors • Increase of FDI from Asian MNEs with similar social and cultural background and more risk taking behaviour • Building-up of 'insider' market position by early entered MNEs in a 'isolated' market situation
1992–95	• Opening of inland cities for FDI and introduction of new ownership forms (e.g. umbrella companies and 'B' share trade) • Liberalization of service sectors to foreign investors • Introduction of micro-level control measures for FDI operations (e.g. transfer pricing, evaluation of non equity contribution for inward FDI and control of state owned assets of Chinese overseas subsidiaries for outward FDI) • Attempts to eliminate unfair competition and improvement of company-level regulations • Towards international standards and national treatment of FDI with upgrading of legal infrastructure (taxation, foreign exchange, company law)	• Increase of efficiency seeking MNEs by using large scale production and process technology and/or creation of own marketing and sourcing subsidiaries • Increase of FDI in infrastructure and business-related service sectors • Diversification into related and unrelated business lines by Asian MNEs as response to booming local market situation • Increase of transfer of organizational capabilities by Western MNEs as result of the internationalization of local business conditions

(NIEs) to relocate their export processing and assembly operations in China while continuing to rely on the transportation and communication facilities of Hong Kong. Based on the experience of the SEZs, the Chinese government in 1984 extended the tax and tariff incentives for foreign companies to fourteen coastal cities, such as Tianjin, Shanghai, Dalian, Guangzhou, etc. and in 1985 to three River Deltas. A number of large MNEs, especially from Japan and to a lesser extent from the USA, were encouraged to transfer manufacturing activities with high capital and technology intensity from their home basis or from other countries to China to benefit from the available lower cost export processing conditions. On the other hand, the opening up of the three River Deltas stimulated companies from the NIEs to integrate their export processing and assembly activities with the small labour intensive domestic enterprises and provided these 'mobile exporters' with local sourcing options at lower costs. It also intensified the integration of these regions into the outsourcing production system of Hong Kong and later of Taiwan, notably in the textile and clothing industry (Sit, 1989, Ash and Kueh, 1993:738).

The setting up of the Hainan SEZ in 1988 and the Pudong economic development zone of Shanghai in 1992 provided foreign investors with an even more liberal investment policy than before. In June 1992, the FDI incentives were extended to eighteen inland provincial-capital cities, five cities along the Yangtze river and thirteen border cities in the North East, South West and North West regions. Recently, seven cities in the Jiangsu province decided to develop the Yangtze River Delta in order to attract high-tech industries, e.g. in petrochemicals, electronics and machine construction. The gradual opening up of these inland cities convinced a number of leading Western multinationals to establish large-scale production units and to introduce a more capital intensive technology in their ventures in China. Some well-established foreign enterprises in China expanded their investment or diversified under the new corporate form of the 'umbrella enterprise' to benefit from both economies of scale and economies of scope within the Chinese market.

The combination of the 'regional development strategy' with the gradual liberalization and upgrading of the specific locational factor endowments has not only largely affected the 'investment development path' of the Chinese regions[6], but also significantly influenced the pattern and extent of the geographic location of foreign EJVs within China (see further).

Ownership structure: The ownership pattern of FDI in China has been influenced by two significant measures which were introduced to diversify the ownership structure of the Chinese economy. First, different forms of FDI — such as equity joint ventures (EJVs), contractual joint ventures (CJVs), wholly foreign owned enterprises (WFOEs), Joint Exploration Activities, Build-operate-transfer (BOT), 'B' share trade, etc. — were gradually extended from the SEZs into the inland regions[7]. Secondly, the development of the private sector, in particular the so-called Town and Village Enterprises (TVEs) and the introduction of ownership reform into the state owned enterprises (SOEs), provided foreign investors with more opportunities to enter into partnerships, particularly with non state owned enterprises. These latter liberalization measures were especially significant for Asian investors who wanted to establish flexible and small scale export oriented production facilities with TVEs.[8].

Although the Chinese EJV Law originally required only a participation of a minimum of 25% by the foreign investor and did not exclude majority participation, the approval of foreign majority owned EJVs was quite exceptional before 1984. Foreign majority EJVs are now explicitly authorized and even promoted, not only in the SEZs but also in the inland provinces. Non-equity control measures in EJVs, such as the restrictions on the management influence of foreign managers within EJVs, were also abandoned with the modification of the EJV Law in 1990.

Sector and performance requirements: Although Chinese FDI policy intended to improve the export performance of its companies and to upgrade the technological capability of China in the global economy, at the beginning the Chinese government did not have a specific sectorial policy vis-à-vis foreign enterprises. As a result, FDI originally was highly concentrated in the service sectors under the form of CJVs, especially in tourism related activities, such as hotels, restaurants and taxi services. Foreign investment in the manufacturing sector reached only 14% of total FDI in 1983 and 33% between 1984-1985. In 1986, the State Council issued the 'Provisions for the Encouragement of Foreign Investment'. These so-called 'twenty-two regulations' attempted to stimulate FDI in import-substitution, export-promotion and advanced technology activities, by facilitating export procedures, providing solutions to the foreign exchange imbalances, limiting external bureaucratic interference and eliminating unfair and costly local interventions.

At the same time, the Chinese FDI regulations became more selective with regard to the 'quality' of FDI, as the 'twenty-two regulations' introduced a set of specific performance criteria, e.g. in terms of export share targets, technology transfer, sector specificity and production requirements. Consequently the relative share of the manufacturing sector in the total FDI increased from 56% during 1986-1988 to 82% during 1989-1991, even after the partial liberalization of the business service sectors (e.g. law, accounting, consulting, finance, banking) in 1992.

In 1995, a more detailed sectorial regulation of FDI was implemented by the Chinese government on the basis of specific categories. First, a so-called 'positive list' includes projects which largely involve the transfer of high-technology and the technical development of leading and basic industries, such as power plants, railways and port infrastructure, machine construction, microelectronics, steel, non ferrous metals and chemicals. Secondly, service sectors — such as telecommunications, aviation, rail and sea transportation — are still discouraged or continue to be prohibited for foreign firms. A third list consists of restricted sectors, including department stores, foreign trade, mining and industries involving monopolies like insurance. The priority sectors will continue to receive tax concessions and preferential access to soft loans (Murray, 1995). However, there are still neither regulatory nor incentive measures to oblige or pressure foreign enterprises to 'localize' R&D activities in China.

Duration of EJV contracts: Although there was no formal limit on the duration of EJVs, the bureaucracy made a distinction between 'productive' (agricultural and manufacturing sectors) and 'non productive' (e.g. tourism related services) projects. In the former case, a period of 25 or more years was acceptable, while in the latter case only 5 to 10 years could be envisaged. However, since 1990 the Chinese government became quite flexible with regard to the determination and extension of the time period for EJVs as other regulatory measures were successively introduced.

8.4 PATTERNS OF EQUITY JOINT VENTURES IN CHINA

Country of origin: About 69% of the EJVs in the data set were initiated by firms from Hong Kong and Macau, as compared with 14% from North America, 8% from Japan and only 4% from EC countries. The results of the oneway analysis of variance showed that there were significant differences among investors according to their country of origin, especially with regard to the size of the project, the foreign equity involvement and the time period of the project (see F-ratio and F-probability in Table 8.2). The Duncan multiple test found significant differences between EJVs from EC countries and those from other nations at the 0.05 level of significance with respect to the size of the investment and the foreign equity contribution.

Table 8.2 Main patterns of EJVs in China by country of origin, location and period of establishment (1979-1990)

		Total investment ('000 US$)		Foreign equity ('000 US$)		Foreign equity share (%)		Duration (years)	
	Number	Mean	SD	Mean	SD	Mean	SD	Mean	SD
A. Country of origin									
EC-12	147	8579.94	21716.18	3597.85	10015.45	40.52	12.08	15.57	7.11
US	492	3778.36	6775.16	1636.44	3263.23	41.71	14.13	14.83	5.66
Japan	291	4309.40	17207.51	2010.16	8586.33	44.72	12.56	14.10	4.89
Hong Kong & Macao	2,199	3006.69	8284.64	1169.72	3760.84	41.46	15.60	13.40	5.91
Singapore	151	3100.32	5524.76	1460.27	2976.98	44.08	13.91	17.17	9.65
ASEAN-4	77	2982.72	5190.05	1395.03	2482.73	47.34	17.22	15.75	8.69
Others	96	4317.28	6774.21	2028.84	3909.25	42.36	11.78	15.07	4.93
F-ratio and F-prob.		7.9017 (0.0000)		7.5437 (0.0000)		4.4976 (0.0002)		14.9127 (0.0000)	
B. Geographic location									
Coastal cities	961	4698.37	12600.83	1999.15	5906.01	42.14	14.68	14.98	6.71
SEZs	645	3117.73	6349.19	1311.79	3190.11	44.89	16.64	15.03	7.32
Eastern region	1,423	3170.23	10343.37	1314.31	4964.18	41.64	14.56	13.36	5.42
Western region	146	2803.25	5771.94	1054.18	2169.07	38.17	14.19	12.82	4.11
Central region	277	2338.24	4795.38	794.75	1159.19	38.64	12.57	12.38	5.10
F-ratio and F-prob.		5.2300 (0.0003)		5.3295 (0.0003)		12.3717 (0.0000)		20.8637 (0.0000)	
C. Period of establishment									
1979-82	78	3523.56	8693.23	1550.68	4047.27	49.68	16.44	13.50	5.98
1983-85	995	4259.77	14951.08	1724.14	6890.45	41.79	14.14	12.86	5.85
1986-88	1,405	2885.64	6669.04	1172.15	3179.56	40.68	13.64	13.79	4.81
1989-90	974	3620.78	7324.47	1566.14	3735.26	43.49	16.98	15.56	7.80
F-ratio and F-prob.		3.7529 (0.0105)		2.9747 (0.0306)		14.4051 (0.0000)		33.2062 (0.0000)	

Source: Database EJVs
Note: SD= Standard Deviation

Investment size: The total investment and the foreign equity contribution of EJVs from EC countries in China averaged about US$8.6 million and US$3.6 million respectively, while these amounts for the whole sample only reached about US$3.5 and US$1.5 million. The crosstabulation analysis showed that nearly half of the EJVs with EC partners were concentrated in the larger sized categories, of which the average investment per project amounted to at least US$2.5 million, as compared with only a third for the total sample.

For the foreign participation in the equity capital, about 22% of the EJVs from the EC committed US$2.5 or more, while this proportion only was 11 percent for the total sample (Table 8.3). The North American EJVs in China were relatively smaller than the Western European ones, but still larger than the mean scores for the complete sample. The distribution of American EJVs in the different size categories was rather homogeneous (as measured by the standard deviation). North American EJV were slightly more concentrated in the middle and large sized categories. While more than 36% of the North American EJVs invested US$2.5 million or more and 38% had a foreign equity commitment of at least US$1 million, in the total sample both of these categories took up about 32%.

The Japanese EJVs are prevalent in the small and medium sized categories, as more than 40% of the Japanese EJVs invested less than US$1 million, as compared to 34% for the total sample. However, the presence of four very large Japanese firms among the top ten EJVs (as compared with only two from the EC) in China as ranked in terms of the value of foreign investment, resulted in higher mean scores of the total and foreign investment for the Japanese firms. Therefore, the size distribution of Japanese EJVs was quite heterogeneous as the value of the standard deviation was much higher than the mean scores. The EJVs established by other Asian investors in China were generally small. The average size of the total investment of EJVs with partners from Hong Kong and Macau was only about US$3 million and the foreign equity investment in these projects was less than US$1.2 million, i.e. the lowest in the sample. While more than 70% of the Hong Kong and Macau EJVs accounted for an investment of less than US$1 million in terms of foreign equity, this proportion was only 55% for the EC and 62% for the US.

Sectorial pattern: The high investment profile of the EC countries is very much related to the specific industrial characteristics of their EJVs in China. While 34% of the EC's EJVs were concentrated in the capital intensive industries (in particular in those with a high level of technology), such as construction materials, transportation and telecom

Table 8.3 Some characteristics of EJVs in China by country of origin (1979-1990)

	EC-12	US & Canada	Japan	HK & Macao	Singapore	ASEAN-4	Other countries	Total	
	%	%	%	%	%	%	%	No.	%
A. Location									
Coastal cities	47.6	29.3	46.4	23.5	32.5	23.4	29.2	961	27.8
SEZs	8.2	10.4	7.9	23.3	17.2	18.2	13.5	653	18.9
Eastern region	36.1	47.0	34.7	40.7	38.4	50.6	44.8	1,424	41.1
Western region	2.7	5.3	4.8	3.9	5.3	0.0	8.3	146	4.2
Central region	5.4	8.1	6.2	8.7	6.6	7.8	13.5	277	8.0
B. Sector									
Agriculture and Mining	4.8	6.3	4.8	3.4	7.3	2.6	3.1	143	4.1
LI-LT	38.1	38.2	42.3	47.6	50.3	66.2	43.8	1,587	45.9
LI-HT	18.4	22.8	16.2	21.2	14.6	11.7	20.8	703	20.3
KI-LT	10.2	10.0	9.3	8.7	11.9	3.9	12.5	316	9.1
KI-HT	23.8	16.1	17.9	10.7	11.9	14.3	14.6	446	12.9
Services	4.8	6.7	9.6	8.4	4.0	1.3	5.2	266	7.7
C. Size of total investment (US$ million)									
0.3	7.5	6.9	9.6	10.1	7.9	5.2	5.2	317	9.2
0.3-0.4	4.8	7.7	12.0	9.5	10.6	14.3	5.2	321	9.3
0.5-0.9	18.4	15.0	18.6	14.7	21.9	20.8	16.7	543	15.7
1-2.4	22.4	33.7	34.7	35.4	27.8	33.8	20.8	1,165	33.7
2.5-4.9	19.7	18.1	14.4	18.0	17.9	10.4	33.3	623	18.0
5 & over	27.2	18.5	10.7	12.3	13.9	15.6	18.8	483	14.0

Table 8.3 Cont.

	EC-12	US & Canada	Japan	HK & Macao	Singapore	ASEAN-4	Other countries	Total	
	%	%	%	%	%	%	%	No.	%
D. Foreign equity investment (US$ million)									
<0.15	11.6	11.6	14.1	15.3	12.6	9.1	7.3	486	14.0
0.15-0.2	14.3	16.5	16.8	17.6	22.5	23.4	17.7	609	17.6
0.3-0.4	13.6	13.2	18.2	15.6	13.9	16.9	12.5	529	15.3
0.5-0.9	15.0	21.1	23.4	22.4	16.6	19.5	10.4	738	21.3
1-2.4	23.1	21.5	16.8	20.0	19.9	16.9	35.4	708	20.5
2.5 & over	22.4	16.1	10.7	9.0	14.6	14.3	16.7	391	11.3
E. Foreign equity share									
5-24.9%	0.0	0.00	0.3	0.8	0.0	1.3	1.0	21	0.6
25-49%	59.2	55.7	46.0	64.7	51.7	46.8	51.0	2,087	60.3
50%	33.3	28.3	37.8	18.8	34.4	27.3	32.3	816	23.6
51-74.9%	6.1	13.6	13.4	10.8	9.9	11.7	15.6	393	11.4
75-100%	1.4	2.4	2.4	4.8	4.0	13.0	0.0	144	4.2

Note: The manufacturing activities of EJVs were divided into four-digit categories following the SIC codes and grouped into subcategories of labour intensive and low technology (LI-HT), labour intensive and high technology (LI-HT), capital intensive and low technology (KI-LT) and capital intensive and high technology (KI-HT). This method of classification was developed and used by Dunning (1979), Lee (1983) and Schroath, Hu and Chen (1993).

Source: Database EJVs

Table 8.4 Some characteristics of EJVs in China by geographic location (1979-1990)

	Coastal cities	SEZs	Eastern region	Western region	Central region	Total	
	%	%	%	%	%	No.	%
A. Sector							
Agriculture and mining	4.2	4.3	4.3	3.4	3.2	143	4.1
LI-LT	40.4	40.7	52.0	47.3	44.4	1,587	45.9
LI-HT	20.0	25.1	18.5	20.5	19.5	703	20.3
KI-LT	10.9	7.4	8.6	9.6	9.7	316	9.1
KI-HT	15.3	11.5	11.5	10.3	16.2	446	12.9
Services	9.3	11.0	5.1	8.9	6.9	266	7.7
B. Size of total investment (US$ million)							
<0.3	7.8	11.3	8.1	13.0	12.6	317	9.2
0.3-0.4	8.0	11.5	9.3	9.6	8.7	321	9.3
0.5-0.9	16.3	14.0	15.5	13.7	20.2	543	15.7
1-2.4	31.3	33.6	35.9	32.2	32.1	1,165	33.7
2.5-4.9	18.2	14.4	19.0	21.9	18.8	623	18.0
5 or more	18.3	15.2	12.2	9.6	7.6	483	14.0
C. Foreign equity investment (US$ million)							
<0.15	12.7	15.3	13.1	21.2	17.0	486	14.0
0.15-0.2	16.3	16.8	17.7	15.1	24.5	609	17.6
0.3-0.4	12.5	15.3	16.7	18.5	15.9	529	15.3
0.5-0.9	20.7	22.7	21.9	18.5	18.8	738	21.3
1-2.4	22.5	17.3	21.4	17.1	17.7	708	20.5
2.5 or more	15.3	12.6	9.2	9.6	6.1	391	11.3
D. Foreign equity share							
5-24.9%	0.3	1.4	0.1	2.7	1.1	21	0.6
25-49%	57.9	53.6	62.3	75.3	66.4	2,087	60.3
50%	25.4	25.4	22.2	15.8	24.2	816	23.6
51-74.9%	12.5	12.1	11.8	2.7	7.9	393	11.4
75-100%	4.0	7.5	3.6	3.4	0.4	144	4.2

Source: Database EJVs

equipment, metal products, chemicals and allied products, this proportion reached only 22% for the total sample (Table 8.3). The sectorial concentration of North American and Japanese EJVs in China somewhat approaches the distribution of the EC firms, as their share in the capital intensive industries reached about 26% and 27% respectively. However, there were some significant differences. Next to the concentration in capital intensive industries, the American EJVs were strongly represented in the high-tech and labour intensive sectors (e.g. machines and precision equipment), while Japanese JV investment was relatively more concentrated in the service activities (9.6% as compared to 7.7% for the mean scores). Hong Kong and Macau's EJVs were relatively more present in the labour intensive industries (69% as compared to 58% for Japan, 61% for North America and 56% for the EC), and dominated the manufacture of textiles and clothing and electrical and electronic assembly operations. The investors from Singapore and other ASEAN countries were relatively more involved in resource related labour intensive production, such as food, paper, basic metals, etc.

The changes in the sector distribution of EJVs in China over the period 1979-1990 were quite evident (Table 8.4). Before the introduction of the '22 regulations' in 1986, EJVs were most typical for the service sectors. While the relative share of the EJVs in the total sample amounted to 26.5% before 1983 and 14.9% during 1983-1985, their relative part only reached 5.5% for the whole period. After 1986, the number of EJVs in manufacturing increased significantly. For instance, EJVs operating in labour intensive and low technological sectors represented about half of all projects between 1986-1990, while before that it was only about 30%. The growth of EJVs in the capital intensive and high tech industries is illustrated by its expanding proportion from 9% during 1983-1986 to 14% during 1986-1990.

Ownership structure: About sixty percent of the EJVs in the sample were minority owned as foreign companies held less than half of the shares in the equity capital. Fifteen per cent were majority owned from abroad, while 24% were equally owned EJVs, i.e. with respectively 50% foreign and 50% Chinese ownership. The EJVs' ownership pattern incurred some substantial changes, however. The equally owned EJVs represented about 40% of all EJVs before 1983 and 30% between 1983-1985, as compared with 24% for the whole period. The foreign owned majority EJVs doubled their relative importance in the total sample from about 12% before 1983 to more than 25% between 1989-1990. The share of the minority EJVs also increased, especially between 1986-1988 (Table 8.4).

The investors from Hong Kong and Macau were relatively more present in the category of the minority owned EJVs, while the other foreign companies, especially those from Japan and the EC countries, preferred relatively more a situation of equal ownership (Table 8.3). The ASEAN-4 (i.e. Indonesia, Malaysia, Philippines and Thailand) and Japanese investors scored significantly different (Duncan test at the 0.05 level) from EC, US and Hong Kong and Macau firms with regard to the degree of ownership. The average level of the equity participation of ASEAN-4 and Japan firms was slightly higher than the mean scores (respectively 47.3% and 44.7% as compared to 42%).

Duration of contract: The average contractual duration of the EJVs in the sample was about 14 years. The contract period for Hong Kong's EJVs of 13.3 years was somewhat shorter than for the EJVs from other countries, in particular those from Singapore (17.2 years), ASEAN-4 (15.7) and the EC countries (15.4). The difference among the investors according to their country of origin was mainly determined by the sectorial distribution of their EJVs. Firms in agriculture and mining and especially financial activities typically covered a longer time period (respectively 15.9, 17.6 and 23.2 years) than those in wholesale and retail trade (9.7 years). In manufacturing, those EJVs that operated in the capital intensive sectors tended to have somewhat longer contract periods (15.2 years) than those in the labour intensive industries (13.5 years).

Geographical location: When the different Chinese regions and cities are grouped into 5 categories — i.e. the five SEZs, the fourteen coastal cities, the Eastern region without the two previous zones, the Central region and Western region — the analysis of their specific locational factor endowments, such as geographic position, level of economic development, industrial infrastructure, and specific FDI incentives, presents some interesting results. The differences among the EJVs according to the regions in which they are located were sometimes quite significant (Tables 8.2 and 8.5).

The large sized EJVs with a high foreign resource commitment operating in capital intensive industries located relatively more in the 14 coastal cities (26% as compared with 19% in SEZs and about 20% in the Eastern and Western regions), while the small and medium sized labour intensive firms with less advanced technology were mainly based in the Eastern region (e.g. three River Deltas) (52% as compared

Table 8.5 Changing patterns of EJVs in China (1979-1990)

	1979-1982	1983-1985	1986-1988	1989-1990	Total	
	%	%	%	%	No.	%
A. Sector						
Agriculture and mining	8.4	6.5	4.0	1.5	143	4.1
LI-LT	28.9	34.0	52.0	50.5	1,587	45.9
LI-HT	12.0	21.8	19.5	20.6	703	20.3
KI-LT	4.8	7.5	10.0	10.0	316	9.1
KI-HT	19.3	8.9	14.0	14.9	446	12.9
Services	26.5	21.2	0.6	2.5	61	7.7
B. Location						
Coastal cities	26.5	25.6	28.5	29.0	961	27.8
SEZs	42.2	22.3	18.9	13.3	653	18.9
Eastern region	24.1	37.8	39.7	48.0	1,424	41.1
Western region	3.6	4.3	4.8	3.3	146	4.2
Central region	3.6	9.9	8.0	6.4	277	8.0
C. Foreign equity share						
5-24.9%	1.2	1.8	0.1	0.00	21	0.6
25-49%	47.0	59.0	62.8	59.2	2,087	60.3
50%	39.8	30.3	23.2	15.8	816	23.6
51-74.9%	3.6	6.3	11.2	17.4	393	11.4
75-100%	8.4	2.6	2.6	7.6	144	4.2

Source: Database EJVs

with about 40% for the coastal cities and SEZs). The firms located in the SEZs were strongly represented in the high-tech labour intensive industries and service sectors, where their relative share amounted to 25% and 9% as compared with an average of 20% and 6%. The size and foreign equity contribution of these EJVs were quite diversified, however. Although there was no significant difference between EJVs located in the Western and Central regions in terms of project size and foreign equity investment, they were quite unlike each other with respect to the sectorial distribution, i.e. the EJVs in the Central region were more concentrated in the capital intensive industries, while those in the Western region were strongly represented in the labour and natural resource intensive industries. The locational patterns of EJVs have also changed. The crosstabulation analysis showed that in the early years EJVs tended to concentrate in the SEZs (42% before 1983 as compared to 19% for the whole period), while they reached a higher profile in the 14 coastal cities and Eastern region after 1986 (Table 8.4).

8.5 CONCLUSION

The analysis of the empirical data showed that the responses of MNEs vis-à-vis the Chinese FDI regulations were quite distinctive according to their FSAs and their strategic positioning. The MNEs from Western industrial countries were mostly engaged into local market oriented production with a high intensity of qualified human resources and a capital intensive technology. When confronted with trade and non-trade barriers in their export endeavours to China, these companies decided to produce within the market itself and followed the import substitution policy of the Chinese government in order to acquire a substantial market share. While, their investment strategies during the early years of the 1980s were more of a 'testing' nature, it was only after the opening up of the 14 coastal cities and the improved access to the local market, that these Western firms started to really engage into large sized and long term oriented EJVs.

The firms from the NIEs, especially from Taiwan and Hong Kong were typical resource (especially cheap labour) seekers in China. They gradually moved all or parts of their export processing activities to China in order to benefit from the supply of unskilled labour which is available at a lower cost than could be obtained in their home market. The FSAs of these firms were mainly linked with their small scale and flexible production technology as well as the specialized skills and capabilities that they acquired within the labour intensive and export oriented industries. The investors from Asian developing countries like ASEAN-4 were mainly present in the processing of raw materials and agricultural activities in China, as their home operations are often still concentrated in resource intensive production. Of course, the distinctions among these different type of investors should not be exaggerated as on the one hand a number of MNEs from industrial countries — especially those from Japan and the US — undertook outsourcing processing operations and on the other hand certain firms from the NIEs were e.g. also engaged into local market oriented production in China.

With respect to ownership structure, the importance of the equity share by the MNEs in their EJV in China seemed to be not only determined by their technological and financial capabilities, but also by their need to acquire local market knowledge. When MNEs from Western countries invested in China for market seeking motives, they were especially concerned with the accessibility of the domestic market (distribution network and market information) and the relationship with the local government (Beamish, 1988). Therefore, these MNEs preferred EJVs with local partners to wholly owned subsidiaries, especially in the early years when the culturally different and complex institutional and bureaucratic environment in China presented serious challenges for newcomers. The dependence of MNEs on the Chinese government for marketing support became weaker and the involvement of Chinese partners into EJVs lessened at the end of the 1980s, with the extension and improvement of the market mechanism into the Chinese economic system (Van Den Bulcke and Zhang, 1994a).

The higher equity stakes that Western MNEs took up in recent years were also related to the nature of their high-tech operations. Wholly or majority owned EJVs allowed them to appropriate the economic rent and to provide more protection against the erosion of their technological lead. These trends confirmed the theoretical predictions and empirical findings of previous studies (e.g. Beamish, 1988, Casson and Zheng, 1990).

The resource and labour seeking investors in China, mostly originate from neighbouring economies and are most often owned and controlled by 'Overseas Chinese'. As they have a similar cultural and social background than the local partners in China, the so-called 'social knowledge' (Sohn, 1993), i.e. personal contacts, family connections, political links, etc, formed a particularly important asset that allowed the Overseas Chinese investors to rely on social means of control instead of the formal control systems used by Western firms. This might be one of the major reasons why their equity stakes in China are lower then for others. Some other factors may explain the preferences for a lower equity position and looser control by Asian investors in China. Firstly, many resource seeking firms from Hong Kong and other NIEs are still in the early stage of the multinationalization process. Secondly, as the labour intensive export processing activities of MNEs from NIEs are often influenced by rapid market changes, non-equity arrangements (e.g. contractual joint ventures or subcontracting) or minority EJVs are often preferred in order to reduce investment risks. Thirdly, the specific activities of the subsidiary and the degree of its integration within the value chain of the parent company also affect ownership control. For instance, the simple integration between the 'offshore' manufacturing processing activities of subsidiaries and parent company's value added chain (i.e. often limited to a trade-manufacturing link across borders) is less dependent on a situation of full ownership to control and coordinate the 'intra-firm's operations. This applies to many parent companies from Hong Kong and Taiwan, where the functions in the home basis were reduced to trade and marketing activities and manufacturing was transferred to China. Fourthly, the local Chinese partners — mostly state owned enterprises or government institutions — may rely on e.g. privileged access to local resources, markets and the administration to control the venture's operation.

As far as the locational decisions are concerned, the market seeking investors tended to establish more closely in the large and densely populated urban areas, especially because the vast Chinese market became gradually more fragmented. As local governments increasingly protect their regional or provincial markets, MNEs have been prompted to abandon their centralized approach and to establish their own marketing network in different regions of the country (Van Den Bulcke and Zhang, 1994b).

The Chinese government apparently carried out the main economic objectives of its FDI policy by using specific regulatory measures with regard to geographic location, export promotion and technology transfer and the sectorial preferences. The impact of MNEs on the Chinese CSAs within the context of the transition of a centrally controlled to a market economic system were quite evident. MNEs certainly contributed to the further development of market mechanisms by 'pushing' the Chinese government to create the necessary market infrastructure and legal framework for business transactions and to stimulate international business standards in firms with forward and backward linkages with the MNEs. Since the last few years, an increasing number of MNEs tended to invest or reorganize their activities on the basis of efficiency considerations and strategic asset seeking. While the 'offshore' export processing activities of MNEs from NIEs in China developed more intensely the local sourcing capabilities, the market seeking investors from Western countries tried to establish integrated local sourcing and marketing networks and to enter into alliances with local firms. These Western firms relied much more on the existence and workability of an efficient market structure, rather than on the tax or tariff incentives, which were originally provided.

Within the context of the increasing liberalization of national economies, MNEs tend to have more and more locational alternatives to efficiently organize their cross-border value-added chain or global business network. The Chinese government is therefore confronted with a double challenge: on the one hand, it has to upgrade the FDI investment climate and improve its created assets on the basis of human capital development and intensive infrastructure in order to allow MNEs to engage into more local market oriented operations and to stimulate them to set-up linkages with local firms. On the other hand, the government has to adjust to the more global FDI strategies of MNEs, because the future development of FDI in China not only depends on the specific measures to 'guide' MNEs into local economic linkages, but also more on the integration of local economies into the global trade and investment network of multinational enterprises.

NOTES AND REFERENCES

1. In the first nine months of 1994 the volume of contracted new FDI reached US$22.72 billion, up 49% as compared with the corresponding period of the previous year (Financial Times, November 7, 1994).
2. The most important impact of FDI on Chinese exports are related on the one hand to the shift of Chinese exports from primary products to labour intensive and sometimes high local value added manufactures and on the other hand to the gradual integration of the Chinese economy into the cross-border networks of intra-industry and intra-firm link-ups (Zhang and Van Den Bulcke, 1995).
3. The other major FDI forms in China are Contractual Joint Ventures (CJVs) and Wholly Foreign Owned Enterprises (WFOEs), of which the relative shares were respectively 26.4% and 21.8% in contracted value and 19.7% and 16% in current value.
4. Similar but less recent data, which were used in other studies on foreign owned enterprises in China, was provided by the China Investment Guide (CITIC, 1984, 1985, 1986). Most of these studies covered the period 1979-1985 (e.g. Beamish, 1988, Campbell, 1989, Casson and Zheng, 1990, Schroath, Hu and Chen, 1993).
5. Term used to indicate the creation of institutional infrastructure that allows the renaissance of market mechanism in the economic system (McMillan, 1993).
6. As a result, the proportion of the Central and Western regions in the total contracted FDI value increased from less than 1% in 1983 to 10% in 1992. The 12 coastal provinces which had opened up first received more than 92% of the total Chinese inward FDI (in terms of current value) at the end of 1992. These coastal provinces in 1994 created already more than 60% of China's GDP.
7. Consequently, the proportion of WFOEs in the total current FDI increased from 5.8% in 1979-1982 to 24% in 1992, while the proportion of CJVs declined from 79% to 20% during the same period. By the end of 1992, 57% of the FDI in China were realized in EJVs (in terms of current value), 19.7% in CJVs and 16% in WFOEs.
8. By the end of 1992, more than 15,000 Chinese TVEs had entered into joint ventures with foreign partners, which represented 18% of all FDI projects (China Statistical Bureau, 1993).

BIBLIOGRAPHY

ASH, R.F. and Y.Y. KUEH (1993) 'Economic Integration within Greater China: Trade and Investment Flows Between China, Hong Kong and Taiwan', *The China Quarterly*, no 136:711-745.

BEAMISH, P. W.(1988) *Multinational Joint Ventures in Developing Countries*, London and New York: Routledge.

CAMPBELL, N.(1989) *A strategicguide to equityjoint venturesin China*, Oxford: Pergamon Press.

CANTWELL, J. (1989) *TechnologicalInnovation and MultinationalCorporation*, Oxford: Basil Blackwell.

CASSON, M. and J. ZHENG (1990) 'Western Joint Ventures in China', *Discussion Paper*, University of Reading.

CITIC (1984-1986) *The China Investment Guide*, Hong Kong: Longman.

CONTRACTOR F. J. (1990) 'Ownership patterns of US joint ventures abroad and the liberalisation of foreign government regulation in the 1980s: evidence from the benchmark surveys, *Journal of International Business Studies*, 21:55-73.

DUNNING J. H. (1979) 'Explaining changing patterns of international production: In defence of the eclectic theory', *Oxford Bulletin of Economics and Statistics*, November: 269—96.

DUNNING, J.H. (1986) 'The investment development cycle and Third World multinationals', in K.M. Khan (ed.) *Multinational of the South: New Actors in the International Economy*, London: Frances Printer, 15-47.

DUNNING, J.H. (1992) 'The global economy, domestic governance, strategies and transnational corporations: interactions and policy implications', *Transnational Corporations*, no 3:7-44.

DUNNING, J.H. (1993) *Multinational Enterprises and the Global Economy*, Wokingham, UK and Reading, Mass.: Addison Wesley.

Financial Times (1994) 'China', *Financial Times Survey*, November 7.

HARROLD, P. and R. LALL (1993) 'China: Reform and Development in 1992—93', *World Bank DiscussionPapers*, No.215, Washington: World Bank.

HEDLUND, G. (1992), 'A Model of Knowledge Management and The Global N-Form Corporation', Paper, *18th Annual Conference of the EIBA*, Reading, UK, December, 13-15.

International Economic Review (1994) 'Foreign Investment in China', July:12-17.

LARDY, Nicholas R. (1994) *China in the World Economy*, Washington, DC: Institute for International Economics, 156p.

LEE, Chung H. (1983) 'International production of the United States and Japan in Korean manufacturing industries: A comparative study', *Weltwirtshaftliches Archiv*, 119 (4):745—53.

McMILLAN, C.H. (1993) 'The role of foreign direct investment in the transition from planned to market economies', *TransnationalCorporations*,no 3:97-119.

MOFTEC (1984-1994) *Almanac of China's foreign economic relations and trade*, Hong Kong.

MURRAY, G. (1995) 'China further restricts foreign investment incentives', *Japan Economic Newswire*, March 24.

OSTRY, S. (1992) 'The domestic domain: the new international policy arena', *Transnational Corporations*, no 1:7-26.

PLASSCHAERT, S. (1989) 'The foreign exchange adequacy requirement for equity joint ventures in the People's Republic of China', in *Dynamics of international business, 15th Annual Conference of EIBA*, Helsinki, p.1156-1173.

PLASSCHAERT, S. and D. VAN DEN BULCKE (1991) 'Changing Dynamics of International Production: An Analysis of Globalization and Collaborative

Developments of Multinational Enterprises', in J. van den Broeck and D. Van Den Bulcke (eds.) *Changing Economic Order*, Groningen: Wolters Noordhoff, 93-116.

SCHROATH, F. W., M. Y. HU and H. Y. CHEN (1993) 'Country-of-Origin Effects of Foreign Investments in the People's Republic of China', *Journal of International Business Studies*, Quarter, 278-290.

SINGH, I. (1992) 'China: Industrial Policies for an Economy in Transition, *World Bank Discussion Papers*, no 143, Washington: World Bank.

SIT, V.F.S.(1989). Industrial Out-processing---Hong Kong's New Relationship with the Pearl River Delta, *Asian Profile*, vol. 17, no 1.

SOHN, J. H. D. (1993) 'Social Knowledge as a Control System: A Proposition and Evidence from the Japanese FDI Behaviour', *Journal of International Business Studies*, Quarter, 296-324.

STOPFORD, J. and S. STRANGE (1991) *Rival States, Rival Firms: Competition for World Market Shares*, Cambridge: Cambridge University Press.

STREETEN, P. (1992) 'Interdependence and integration of the world economy: the role of States and firms', *Transnational Corporations*, no 1:125-136.

UNCTAD (1994) *World Investment Report 1994*, New York: United Nations.

UNCTC (1993) *World Investment Report 1993*, New York: United Nations.

VAN DEN BULCKE, D. (1988) 'Deregulation of Foreign Direct Investment in Developing Countries', in D. Van Den Bulcke (ed) *Recent Trends in International Development: Direct Investment, Services, Aid and Human Rights*, Antwerp: University of Antwerp, 29-63.

VAN DEN BULCKE, D. and H. ZHANG (1994a) 'Belgian Equity Joint Ventures in China, Some Considerations and Evidence' in S. Stewart (ed) *Joint Ventures in the People's Republic of China, Advances in Chinese Industrial Studies*, vol. 4, JAI-Press, p.165-183.

VAN DEN BULCKE, D. and H. ZHANG (1994b) 'The Development of Local Marketing Knowledge within Joint Ventures: An Analysis of the Performance of Belgian Multinationals in China' in K. Obloj (ed.) *High Speed Competition in a New Europe, Proceedings of the 20th Annual Conference of EIBA*, vol. 2, Warsaw: International Postgraduate Management Center, University of Warsaw, 129-162.

YIP, G. S. (1989) 'Global Strategy in a World of Nations?', *Sloan Management Review*, Fall:29-41

ZANDER, I. and O. SÖLVELL (1992), 'Transfer and Creation of Knowledge in Local Firm and Industry Clusters-Implications for Innovation in the Global Firm', Paper, *AIB Annual Meeting*, Brussels, November 21-22.

ZHANG, H. and D. VAN DEN BULCKE (1995) 'Rapid Changes in the Investment Development Path of China' in J. H. Dunning and R. Narula (eds.) *Foreign Direct Investment and Governments, Catalysts for Economic Restructuring*, Routledge, p. 380-422.

9 Regions of Europe: The Feasibility of a New Administrative Status

Jacques Drèze

9.1 REGIONS OF EUROPE AS A CONCEPT

9.1.1 Definition

By the 'Status of Region of Europe' (SRE) I mean a legal, political and administrative structure whereby a geographical area, currently part of the territory of a member state of the European Community (EC), could henceforth belong to the Community directly, without being any longer part of a member state. Residents of that region would, under appropriate conditions, be *citizens of Europe*, without deriving that quality from their citizenship of a member state. Yet this status would be organized by and within the EC as it now exists, namely as a 'Europe of Nations'.

Of course, important modifications and additions to the treaties organizing the EC would be required for the implementation of an SRE – starting with the article of the Maastricht Treaty defining European citizenship. And the new treaty or treaties would need to be ratified by all member states. I do not speculate, in this chapter, about the immediate political realism of the new status. My purpose is limited to defining the concept and discussing the conditions under which its implementation could be Pareto-improving. A parallel discussion of other – especially political – dimensions is obviously called for.

The possibly novel viewpoint developed here is that there is room for 'Regions of Europe' within a 'Europe of Nations'. There is no compelling reason why a move towards a 'Europe of Regions' should proceed synchronously over the whole territory of the EC. It is conceptually feasible to organize the Community on a flexible basis, allowing simultaneously for the continuation of the current set-up and for the existence of 'post-national' entities organized under the new status.

9.1.2 Illustrations

Andorra is a small territory straddling the border between France and Spain, with a population of some 13,000 inhabitants (plus some 26,000 guest workers). Until recently it lived under an idiosyncratic status, formally headed by two 'co-princes', the President of France and the Bishop of Urgel. In March 1993, a constitutional reform took Andorra close to political autonomy. If Andorra were to become an independent nation, it could either stay outside the EC or seek admission as a 16th Member state. Would it not be more practical for Andorra to become an autonomous region of Europe, directly attached to the Community?

Corsica derives substantial benefits from its current status as two French departments. Yet, that status is not unanimously appreciated. Some Corsicans resent dependence vis-a-vis France, and the situation occasionally becomes 'explosive', with a serious loss of welfare for residents, visitors, property owners, etc. Some also claim that the situation of dependence leads to inefficiencies, and that if the Corsicans were fully responsible for their own fate, local initiative might speed up development. The menu of alternatives consists of either greater autonomy within the French Republic, or Corsican independence. As a 'Region of Europe', Corsica would cease to be part of France, without, however, becoming a sovereign state. Instead, it would rely on the EC to supply the basic 'services' invariably provided by the federal authorities under existing constitutions: citizenship and its external protection, a currency, defence, diplomatic representation and the like. (see further) To become a 'Region of Europe' might be more attractive to Corsicans than either gaining added autonomy within France, or going to the trouble and expense of organizing an autonomous state. A point could be reached where the French themselves prefer not having to deal any longer with Corsican frictions. From the viewpoint of the EC, inheriting Corsica as a Region might be preferable to inheriting Corsica as another member state. Therefore, the concept of SRE is indeed worth discussing.

As a third illustration, I shall (not surprisingly) mention Belgium. There are two reasons for doing so. First, the head of the Flemish government anticipates only three meaningful levels of political responsibility: municipal, regional (Flanders) and European. He has also stated implicitly that a convincing step in that direction could not wait for the emergence of a 'Europe of Regions'. Wallonia, which has no declared vocation to become a nation, would find its own range of alternatives propitiously enlarged if an SRE were in sight. Second, if it survives as a largely decentralized federal nation, Belgium will need to settle the fate of Brussels, which currently fits into the evolving institutions of Belgium like a square peg in a round hole. For the seat of the European Commission a 'District of Brussels' comparable to the American 'District of Columbia' may some day appear natural.

In what follows, I consider exclusively the prospect of a change of status decided cooperatively — say, in my second example, on the basis of a parliamentary vote in Paris and a referendum in Corsica. Such a prospect may seem unrealistically remote. But what seems farfetched today may still be imposed by circumstances tomorrow! An early discussion of the new alternative is needed, and it can best take place without the pressure from a specific crisis.

9.1.3 Justification

The last two examples also illustrate the potential dangers of the proposed discussion. Most probably, the existence of an SRE would exert some influence on the dynamics of the Corsican or Belgian situations. It might also have an impact on the dynamics of European integration. In both cases, there are positive as well as negative aspects. I am not claiming that the merits of an SRE outweigh the drawbacks or dangers. I am only claiming that the potential merits invite a further investigation of how an SRE would work, and what the main pitfalls might be.

The basic justification for the further investigation is simply, as already stated above, the provision of an enlarged choice set to those regions of Europe which seem to be ill-at-ease under prevailing arrangements. After all, national boundaries are outcomes of historical hazards which have survived the test of time; this is a weak case for rationality.

An SRE would be the best outcome if (i) more regional autonomy is a *potential* source of efficiency gains and (ii) the SRE would, in some cases, provide a more efficient framework for the exercise of regional autonomy than either political independence or added autonomy within existing nations. The first assertion is commonplace. It is a logical tautology, with the proper emphasis on 'potential'. Because local decisions could always replicate centralized decisions, their results could not be inferior at unchanged opportunities. I come back in Section 2 to the twin issues of where the autonomy pays, and where the opportunities may differ. The second assertion is not commonplace, to the best of my knowledge, since I have not seen any explicit reference to an SRE.[1] It seems obvious that such a status could easily dominate political independence, especially in the case of small regions; small by the size of their population like Corsica (250,000 inhabitants, compared with Luxembourg's 370,000) or by area like Brussels (roughly comparable in size to Washington's District of Columbia or to Monaco). On the other hand, it is less clear that the new status (SRE) offers opportunities that go beyond those consistent with added autonomy within existing nations. I shall return to that issue in the conclusion.

The investigation which I am proposing is limited to a specific aspect of a more general problem. Take a set of regions (for instance the 71 regions of EC 12 using the NUTS 1 statistical level), and consider all possible partitions. Each partition is an array of nations. One could then attempt to compare the merits of alternative partitions, i.e. alternative groupings of regions into nations. (One could play the game of 'recombining' the regions into nations.) And one could even do this under alternative constitutions differentiated by degrees of regional autonomy within nations as well as by degrees of international cooperation among nations. (This could also be labelled degrees of internal and external federalism.)[2] Short of tackling that formidable global problem, one could compare 'adjacent partitions', obtained by transferring a single region from one nation to another. Or one could define conditions under which a transfer is Pareto-improving, and study the properties of sequences of Pareto-improving transfers. I am looking at the very special case where attention is restricted to transfers of regions from preexisting nations to a hypothetical entity called 'Regions of Europe'. The nature of the issues arising in that special case is illustrative of those that would arise in the more general problem just outlined. My interest is centred on the prospects for Pareto-improvements.

9.2 FEASIBILITY

9.2.1 Legal alternatives

There are two approaches to providing a legal, political and administrative structure for 'Regions of Europe': a traditional approach and an innovative approach.

The first approach would consist in organizing, within the traditional framework of international law, a new nation pulling together the Regions of Europe aspiring to the new status. Call the new nation FRE (for 'Federated Regions of Europe'). The originality of that new nation would consist in (a) pushing to the limit the decentralization possibilities offered by a federal constitution — with only a minimal set of functions carried out at the federal (central) level; (b) being 'open-ended', that is, being prepared to admit other 'Regions of Europe' (in addition to those initially federated) as members of the federation — under minimal conditions. Three minimal conditions come to mind: (i) being geographically part of the European Community; (ii) adhering to the FRE constitution; and (iii) seceding from a member state of the EC, to join the FRE, through a democratic, legal process (as opposed, say, to a revolutionary process). The new nation might come into existence because Andorra or Corsica becomes independent and creates the FRE rather than creating a local republic; or because Belgium adopts the new denomination and changes its constitution according to principles (a) and (b) above; or as a consequence of any comparable developments acceptable to the EC, of which the new nation would be a member on par with other national member states.

The alternative, more innovative approach, would consist in establishing within the EC the 'Status of Region of Europe' (SRE) whereby, subject to the same minimal conditions mentioned above, some regions would belong to the EC directly, as 'post-national entities'. Under this approach, the minimal functions attended to under (a) above would be performed by the Community itself on behalf of these regions, without federating them into a traditional nation. Some imagination would need to be exercised in creating the legal, political and administrative structure defining the SRE. The exercise seems worthwhile as a step beyond nationalism.

9.2.2 Centralized functions

The practical implications of both approaches are largely parallel, and I will limit myself to the SRE approach. In order to give content to the discussion, I will review briefly some of the centralized functions to be provided, namely: citizenship, diplomatic (international) representation, a currency and defence.

Article 8 of the Maastricht Treaty institutes a 'European Citizenship'; it stipulates that all nationals of a member state, and only such persons, are citizens of Europe. As indicated in Section 9.1.1, the SRE would need to be instituted by a new treaty among member states. That treaty would in particular amend article 8 and stipulate, say, that European Citizenship is retained, when an area becomes a Region of Europe, by all residents who give up (or lose) their citizenship of a member state. To illustrate, if Corsica were to become a Region of Europe, French citizens residing in Corsica could give up their French citizenship while retaining their European citizenship, with all the implications spelled out in article 8 (mainly, freedom of circulation and establishment, voting rights and eligibility in elections at municipal level or for the European Parliament in the country of residence within the entire EC, diplomatic or consular assistance outside the EC from representatives of all member states). The Regions of Europe should elect directly a suitable number of representatives to the European Parliament. Eventually (numbers justifying), the Regions of Europe could be represented directly in the Commission and Council(s).

The Commission would supervise the administration of citizenship under the SRE, issue passports (through local offices), and regulate the acquisition of citizenship through immigration from outside the EC, or the conservation of European citizenship in case of migration within the EC. (Of course, the acquisition of national citizenship in a member state by a regional citizen of Europe would remain subject to the currently prevailing legislation).

The protection of citizen's rights has two aspects, namely the domestic protection of civil (constitutional) rights and the external protection. Domestic protection could be entrusted to the European Court of Justice which, according to article 177, is already competent to interpret statutory provision of organisms created by the Council of Ministers of the EC. The SRE could be added to that domain of competence, or an appropriate alternative could be organised, so as to protect regional citizens of Europe against abuse by regional authorities. Clearly, I am here out of my depth, as legal expertise is called for.

External protection could be entrusted to diplomatic or consular representatives of any Member State. Numbers justifying, representatives of the EC as such could exercise consular functions on behalf of Regions of Europe. The SRE could, and probably should organize such a possibility.

Regions of Europe should not create their own currencies, but should instead use the ECU according to the so-called 'currency board' principle;[3] bank(s) could issue ECU-notes on the basis of 100 per cent reserves of the constituting national currencies. These notes would be legal tender in the Regions of Europe, where bank accounts would normally be denominated in ECUs (but could also be denominated in other currencies, as elsewhere). Banking regulations within regions of Europe would be administered by the Commission. The Regions would implement full mobility of capital. Being deprived of policy instruments, they would abstain from pursuing autonomous monetary objectives. Such an arrangement does not seem to raise special problems. Which bank(s) might issue ECU-notes is an open matter, to be settled in a practical way (taking into account the availability of spare capacity of printing equipment as well as institutional reliability).

Regarding defence I again feel out of my depth. It would be for the EC to decide whether or not it wishes to use this opportunity to organize a small specialized force — normally under the authority of the Western European Union (WEU). That issue can 'safely' be postponed until later.

9.2.3 Potential drawbacks

None of the issues raised above seems to cast serious doubt about the operational *feasibility* of an SRE. Of course, there is scope for investigating the operational *efficiency* of the centralized functions, under alternative arrangements.

The crucial issues lie elsewhere. What is at stake is a new possibility of redefining the boundaries of nations, within Europe, whenever aspirations towards local autonomy conflict with national institutions. The crucial issue is whether the (efficiency) gains of decentralization outweigh the potential drawbacks of the proposal. I see two main drawbacks, namely: (i) the risk of destabilizing performing national entities under regional pressures of debatable legitimacy; (ii) the risk of bending the process of European integration in uncertain directions. I discuss safeguards against these drawbacks in Section 9.4, and how they could be compared with the gains in Section 9.5. Before that, I wish to explore the economic dimension of the proposal.

9.3 ECONOMIC DESIRABILITY

9.3.1 Distributive, allocative and stabilizing dimensions

If region *R* seceded from nation *N* to become a Region of Europe, some functions previously exercised by Nation *N* over the territory or on behalf of the residents of region *R* will be taken over, either by region *R* itself, or by some European authority. In order to sort out the economic aspects of such a transfer of competence and responsibilities, it is helpful to borrow the well-known distinction used by Musgrave (1959) between the distributive, allocative and stabilizing functions of governments. Applying that distinction to the functions to be transferred, and only to these, I think that the contents of the three categories can be defined recursively with logical sharpness – even if serious measurement problems remain to be faced.

It is helpful to think about all the activities of a government as reflected in public receipts and expenditures. To simplify, let us consider the class of activities for which receipts and expenditures have a well-defined regional identification – like taxes levied on local property, firms or residents; expenditures on local schools and roads or in the form of transfers to residents, etc. The allocative function concerns the real activities underlying these receipts and expenditures. I shall take the view that, insofar as specifically regional aspects are concerned, the distributive and stabilizing functions are reflected in the regional aggregates of receipts and expenditures, and can be discussed in terms of these alone.

The distributive function of a central government implements transfers among the regions under its jurisdiction, in principle to correct inequality in the distribution of needs and resources among these regions. In part, these redistributive transfers result from the national tax-and-transfers legislation applicable to households (or to other microeconomic units, like firms or municipalities). If the sum of these transfers over the households located in region *R* were equal to zero, and the sum for the whole nation were also zero, then one could conclude that region *R* is not participating (on that score) in interregional transfers. Whatever redistribution is taking place among households is then internal to the region, and could be continued on a regional basis in case of secession. In general, however, there exist redistributive transfer among regions — in particular because the personal distributions of family incomes, or family situations conducive to transfer, are not the same in different regions. When the sums over all regions of the relevant receipts and expenditures are equal, redistributive transfers add up to zero. These redistributive transfers are measured, in that case, by the discrepancy between aggregate receipts and expenditures of each region. That is also the amount which a region should receive from, or could contribute to, the central government while continuing to carry out the same allocative functions and the same distributive or stabilizing function *internal to the region* (i.e. lacking an interregional dimension).

For the purposes of this section, I shall assume that redistributive transfers add up to zero and are thus well-defined. The more general case is the subject of Section 9.4, which is devoted to successive extensions. The stabilizing function concerns the ability of a central government to organize mutual insurance among the regions under its jurisdiction, so that idiosyncratic shocks affecting individual regions are partly absorbed through transfers between the regions. In practice, it is often difficult to draw the line between insurance payments and redistributive transfers, and that distinction is not introduced into the underlying legislation. From a logical viewpoint, however, the distinction is possible. If there existed insurance markets assigning well-defined values to shock-dependent transfers (to 'state-contingent claims' in the technical terminology of economic theory), then a property of the mutual insurance components would be that their present net value on the insurance markets is zero. Any departure from the zero market value would be indicative of a redistributive element. I explain below (Section 9.3.3) why the opportunities for mutual insurance might be reduced in case e.g. a region *R* secedes from nation *N*.[4]

These recursive, definitions lead me to treat under the allocative function those activities or policies of a central government that have a regional dimension, when considered net of the redistributive and stabilizing aspects. The costs and benefits of regional autonomy should then be assessed in terms of efficiency of these activities at an unchanged aggregate balance of receipts and expenditures.

9.3.2 Allocative gains of decentralization

The nature of allocative costs and benefits of decentralization (as considered in the literature on fiscal federalism, e.g. Oates, 1972) can be illustrated through a simple example. Corsica has one university, located in Corte, which operates within the legal and administrative set-up of France. In particular, programmes, degrees, staffing, tuition fees and salaries are all decided at the national level in Paris. One of the benefits of autonomy lies in the ability to depart from national norms, in the hope of promoting more effectively local welfare. Because the French university system is organized on a highly centralized basis,[5] there is scope for such benefits — for instance, through regional differentiation of programmes, fees or salaries. These benefits could be assessed in a first stage at unchanged net expenditures; in a second stage, reallocations of net expenditures between alternative regional public activities (universities vs elementary schools vs police protection or public parks) could be considered, within the same overall regional budget. Any redistributive or stabilizing aspect could be viewed as belonging under these functions, kept constant in the aggregate. It is indeed one of the potential benefits of regional autonomy (decentralization) that it tends to eliminate *rent-seeking activities*, whereby regions use opportunities available under the allocative function, not because they are valuable in themselves, but because they are conducive to redistributive transfers. Such would be the case, for instance, if the University of Corte offered a degree in some field attracting very few students (who could more economically be offered scholarships to study elsewhere), simply because the national legislation offers this opportunity — the main benefit of which for the region would come from the additional expenditure boosting the local economy.[6]

The legal and administrative set-up of French universities is a public good. Should Corsica wish to administer its single university autonomously, it would have to bear the corresponding costs, which are hard to assess. The experience of countries like the US, with a large number of private universities, suggests that the cost of running an independent university is small.

The point of this particular example is that the allocative costs and benefits of regional autonomy need careful evaluation. In my example, a fairly definite answer based on experience seems possible. But other areas are less transparent. How should we assess the costs of an independent legislature? Beyond the direct costs (running elections, paying representatives, organizing sessions), one should recognise the fixed costs associated with the existence of legislation: the law must be published; it will then be studied and commented on by experts whose time is valuable; text books and other material will be written, and so on.

Have such matters been studied? The treatments I have seen are fairly general (Oates, 1972, devotes less than two pages to his section on 'The costs of collective decision-making') yet there is ample experience with federal constitutions. Some relevant questions are: how do the costs of law-making, law-enforcement and government relate to country size (in particular, what are relevant measures of size?) In which areas can a country exploit at low cost the experience of others? (In drug administration? In the training of public servants? In public works, public transportation, forest administration? In health and education?)

9.3.3 Loss of stabilizing coinsurance

It seems appropriate at this stage to explain why the *interregional* stabilizing function would be impaired by regional autonomy. Consider for example the case for decentralizing unemployment compensation programmes. There is scope for divergence of opinions regarding the appropriate design of such programmes: what should be the level of unemployment benefits? How should it relate to previous earnings, to duration of unemployment, to age or to family status? What eligibility conditions should be imposed? Should the programme be financed exclusively from contributions based on wage bills? Should such contributions be experience-rated? How should abuses be controlled? The most appropriate design probably varies from region to region — reflecting the nature of unemployment, the composition of the employed and unemployed groups, the social objectives pursued in the regions, etc. At the same time, the design of the programme has implications for the level of activity in the region and hence for other receipts (income and labour taxes, VAT), or expenditures (relief transfers to unemployed not eligible for benefits ...).

It may also be that the implementation of a given programme will be more efficient if the regional authorities in charge regard themselves as financially responsible. If the cost of the programme falls on the regional budget, the motivation for running the programme tightly will be greater than would be the case if the cost falls on a national budget. On the other hand, a national system of unemployment compensation implements a form of mutual insurance against region-specific shocks affecting employment. For instance, Corsica is more (respectively less) sensitive to shocks affecting the demand for tourism (respectively for steel or textiles, i.e. durables) than the region Nord-Pas-de-Calais; the cost of unemployment compensation associated with these shocks is spread through the national system over the entire nation.

Thus mutual insurance is made possible by the existence of uniform national rules applicable to (in) all the participating regions. When the rules are set autonomously at the regional level, a moral hazard problem arises. If region *R* adopts on its own more lax rules, resulting in higher expected costs of its unemployment compensation programme, whereas the other regions stick to tighter rules, it would be unreasonable to ask the other regions to bear most of the additional costs associated with unilateral decisions by region *R*. Insurance is based on the idea that the risks should not be aggravated through the behaviour of the insured; when such aggravation is possible, insurance becomes difficult, and typically ceases to exist.

There is a clear-cut dilemma here. Either regions agree to participate in a national scheme with uniform rules, in which case mutual insurance is possible; or regions wish to adopt differentiated schemes under their own control, in which case they must forego mutual insurance and fully bear their own risks. There is a trade-off between allocative efficiency, fostered by regional differentiation and financial responsibility, and risk-sharing efficiency, achieved through mutual insurance permitted by the adoption of uniform rules. The existence of conflict between allocative efficiency and risk-sharing efficiency is not unusual; the field of unemployment compensation itself is a clear example (see Drèze, 1990, 1993a, and Drèze and Gollier, 1993). A simple example can be given in (Drèze, 1993b, Appendix A), which shows that for large degrees of aversion to risk, or for large variance of productivity shocks, mutual insurance becomes definitely attractive. It is shown that second-best optimal mutual insurance may well be partial insurance: by pooling only a fraction of the risks, an efficient compromise between effort and risk-sharing is obtained.[7]

Of course, the moral hazard difficulty disappears for insurance contracts written, not in terms of final outcomes, but in terms of exogenous contingencies. Thus, Corsica *(C)* and Nord-Pas-de-Calais *(NPC)* could well enter into an insurance contract whereby *NPC* pays an indemnity to *C* if the European market for tourism is depressed, whereas *C* pays an indemnity to *NPC* if the European market for durables is depressed. In practice, contracts of that type are not likely to come up.[8]

Thus regional autonomy may entail a loss of welfare through reduced opportunities for risk-sharing, especially in the case of a rather specialized region seceding from a well-diversified nation.

9.3.4 Distributive neutrality

The conclusion is that if a region *R* were to secede from a nation *N* and become a 'Region of Europe', it would hope to reap some benefits of an allocative nature, by gearing public activities or policies more closely to the local situation (needs and means) and to local preferences, and by controlling more tightly activities for which it becomes financially responsible. These benefits should be evaluated on a net basis, taking account of the costs of collective decision-making (in the region, the nation and the European Community). At the same time, region *R* would lose the benefit of mutual insurance with other regions of nation *N*. All these costs and benefits are real. The desirability of secession hinges on the balance of these costs and benefits.

At the same time, secession would have distributive implications, if there existed (positive or negative) net transfers between region *R* and nation *N*. If properly defined (in particular, if properly distinguished from mutual insurance settlements), these distributive transfers have no real cost. Being in the nature of lump-sum transfers they could in principle be continued after the secession, or discontinued in the absence of secession, at no immediate costs or savings of real resources.

It follows that the presence of regional distributive transfers should not affect the secession decisions, if these are to be guided by a criterion of Pareto improvement. If the region of Lombardy is currently delivering a positive transfer to the rest of Italy, and wishes to secede in order to discontinue that transfer, while possibly incurring as a consequence real costs in excess of real benefits, then it could not be claimed that the secession is Pareto improving – neither effectively, nor even potentially (i.e. under the compensation principle), since Lombardy could not profitably compensate the rest of Italy for the discontinuation of the transfer, under the assumed negative balance of real costs and benefits. (That the Italian region of Lombardy might still be tempted to secede in order to escape the transfer is another story).

I shall therefore introduce as a condition of distributive neutrality that secession of region *R* from nation N should not affect the aggregate transfers between the region and the rest of the nation. Such a condition imposes a form of stability on the process: if only separations that are Pareto-improving in terms of real costs and benefits are implemented, no 'cycling' will occur and the process should converge. Thus, the risk of destabilizing performing national entities under regional pressures of debatable legitimacy, or of starting an endless process of successive divisions, will be largely obviated. Distributive neutrality is the subject of Section 9.4.

9.3.5 The European point of view

Looking at these issues from the standpoint of a set of Regions of Europe, to be joined by some region *R*, is simpler. Under maximal decentralization, the allocative functions would be mostly vested at the regional level, with little or no spillover to the other regions on that score. (If there exist fixed costs of running an FRE or organizing an SRE, it would be advantageous to share these among more regions; but these considerations are apt to be of ancillary significance.) On the distributive front, it seems natural to impose that a region *R* joining a set of other regions – on either the FRE or the SRE basis – should not thereby implement a significant transfer between itself and the other regions. A positive transfer (from *R* to the other regions) would dissuade *R* from joining, a negative transfer would dissuade the other regions from accommodating *R*.

What about mutual insurance among Regions of Europe? In principle, there is scope here for benefits from risk-sharing – subject however to the problem of moral hazard discussed in Section 9.3.3. A scheme of partial insurance, maintaining some (substantial) regional incentives for efficiency could alleviate that problem. Is it conceivable that European authorities define common standards (essentially, for social security provisions and taxation) on to the basis of which mutual insurance among Regions of Europe could be organized?

Short of answering that difficult question, let me note that risk-sharing is generally the more effective, the broader the basis on which risks are pooled. This is an implication of Borch's theorem on mutual insurance; see Borch (1962), Arrow (1963) or Drèze (1990). The implication should be stated carefully, however. Whether it is more advantageous for a specific region *R* to engage in mutual insurance with a specific nation *N* or with the entire EC (of which *N* is a part) depends upon the correlations of shocks specific to *R* with shocks affecting *N* and with shocks affecting the EC. For instance, it could happen that the first correlation is negative whereas the second one is negligible. On the other hand, if a set of Regions of Europe were to contemplate, either organizing internally a scheme of mutual insurance involving member regions only, or organizing such a scheme between member regions and the rest of the EC, then it follows unambiguously from Borch's theorem that the broader basis (weakly) dominates the narrower one.

Whether and how a form of insurance could be organized to limit the exposure of Regions of Europe to idiosyncratic risks is an intriguing question, to which I have no definite answer. My tentative comments are offered in Section 9.5.

9.4 DISTRIBUTIVE NEUTRALITY

9.4.1 A simple example

Is it possible to define with some generality the terms and conditions under which, *ceteris paribus*, any region *R* may secede from the nation *N* of which it is currently a part and become a region of Europe, in such a way that there are *no distributive incentives* in favour of, or against, secession – either from the viewpoint of region *R* or from that of nation *N*? In searching for this form of 'distributive neutrality', I start from a hypothetical streamlined problem, corresponding to a stationary situation, and then introduce successive complications to make the problem more realistic.[9]

Consider a country made up of a number of regions. In each

region, the primary budget (the public budget net of interest payments) may be in surplus or in deficit. The nation's overall primary budget balance is simply the sum of all regions' primary budget balances. To start with, I assume that incomes, population, the real interest rate and the national public debt are all constant. This implies that the overall primary surplus (or deficit) is equal to the interest payment on the national public debt (or the interest income earned on net public assets).

Distributive neutrality in the case of secession or break-up of the nation can be uniquely and unambiguously defined: each region *i* is given a portion a_i of the national debt, where a_i is simply the share of the region's primary budget balance PB_I in the national primary budget balance PB_N:

$$a_i = PB_i \,/\, PB_N \qquad [1]$$

Under this scheme, each region can go on carrying the same levels of spending and receipts and yet its overall budget will remain balanced. The once-and-for-all transfer of public debt allows each and every net family income (after taxes and transfers) to be unchanged. Note that if the nation as a whole was running a primary surplus, a_i is positive if region *i*'s budget is in surplus, negative if region has a deficit on its primary budget. A negative a_i means that region *i* is given assets (IOUs) by the other regions collectively.

9.4.2 Defining net transfers

In the previous case there was no compelling general way of defining interregional transfers. Only if the net national public debt is nil can regional primary balances be considered as transfers (positive or negative) to the rest of the nation. When there exists a net public debt, however, the situation is less clear. To say that region *i* makes a net contribution to the rest of the nation would be equivalent to saying that region *i* contributes a primary balance exceeding its 'normal' share of the interest charges. How should such a 'normal share' be defined? The answer is not obvious, even under my extreme simplifying assumptions.

To see this, consider first simple intuitively appealing criteria, like income or population. The income criterion would define the 'normal share' as the region's proportion of national income. Interregional transfers would thus be defined by comparing, between region *i* and the whole nation, the primary balances expressed as percentages of income: those regions with relative primary balances in excess of the national figure would be net contributors, the others would be net beneficiaries. If instead shares reflect the size of population, a net contribution would arise when a region's primary balance exceeds the national figure more than proportionately to its population. The two results will differ, unless income per capita is the same in all regions.

Why would one criterion be preferred over the other? In trying to answer that question, one might wish to look at either income, or population, as an indicator of 'economic ability' to service the debt. But that line of reasoning leads logically to regard the primary balance as the natural indicator of 'ability to pay': it is an indicator reflecting ability as implicitly assessed by the prevailing tax-and-transfers legislation. If that indicator is used, we are back to formula (1), which implies by construction that there are *no* interregional transfers.

These examples illustrate the difficulty of defining interregional transfers unambiguously when the nation's public debt is not nil. Since my main interest concerns 'distributive neutrality', I do not pursue the topic further here. It could undoubtedly be taken up less gnostically than I have done.

9.4.3 Growth and initial imbalance

Now consider the case when incomes, public spending and receipts in each region all grow at the same rate. The ratio of national public debt to national income will be constant – hence the debt will be sustainable – if the primary surplus covers a fraction of the interest charges on the debt, equal to the relative excess of the nominal interest rate over the nominal growth rate. Then it remains true that 'distributive neutrality' calls for assigning to a seceding region a share of the national debt defined by (1), i.e. equal to the share of the region in the national primary surplus.

What if the initial primary surplus is such that the debt-GDP ratio is not constant? The simplest approach consists in calculating the percentage adjustment in both receipts and expenditures which would stabilize the debt-GDP ratio. Applying the same percentage adjustment to each region[10] leads to a unique rule for apportioning the national debt. The 'distributively neutral' debt-sharing rule is now a weighed average of two ratios: the same ratio a_i of primary deficits as before, and the ratio b_i of total public activity measured as the sum of receipts R_i and spending E_i in the region i relatively to receipts R_N and spending E_N at the national level:

$$b_i = R_i + E_i / R_N + E_n \qquad [2]$$

The term a_i receives a weight of 100 per cent when the national primary budget is at the level which stabilizes the debt-GDP ratio, and below (resp. above) 100 per cent when the primary surplus is insufficient (resp. more than sufficient) for debt sustainability. Thus the correction factor b_i receives a weight equal to the initial departure from sustainability of the debt-GDP ratio. As for the ratios themselves, one could say that a_i measures the relative 'ability to pay' off region *i* whereas b_i measures its relative 'ability to adjust'.

Implicitly so far, when the debt-GDP ratio is sustainable, its level is immaterial. That logic is far from compelling. It is definitely not consistent with the Maastricht rules of fiscal discipline, which put an absolute ceiling on the debt-GDP ratio, instead of imposing its 'sustainability'.[11]

9.4.4 Status of the neutrality condition

The motivation of permitting Pareto-improving reorganizations without creating a source of permanent instability seems highly relevant. On the other hand, if a region with a negative primary surplus wished to secede from a nation with a sustainable public debt, the principle developed here would have the nation issue additional debt and donate the proceeds to the region. The secession should be accompanied by a capital transfer equal to the present value of the future transfers expected to flow from the nation to the region in the absence of secession. This sounds a bit like eating one's cake and having it too!

Of course, I am here assuming that the regional budget did reflect accepted and honestly applied national legislation (as well as local needs and resources, of course). Clearly, if there was agreement that the national legislation was inadequate, it would seem reasonable to revise that legislation first, and then to define distributive neutrality on the revised basis. Similarly, if it were claimed that the national legislation was not applied honestly, it would be imperative to make allowance for the bias. *Nemo turpitudinem suam invocans creditur*

(No benefit can credibly be claimed on the basis of one's own turpitude). Still, to say that a region's primary deficit reflects honest application of a nation's accepted legislation is not to say that the region is automatically entitled to claim a capital transfer equal to the present value of future national contributions to that deficit.

Any practical situation is apt to involve an element of asymmetry. If a relatively rich region (like Lombardy) wished to secede from its nation to become a Region of Europe, it would seem appropriate to apply the reasoning of this section and impose the resulting capital transfer as a condition for the secession and for access to the new status. If instead a relatively poor region (like Corsica) wished to secede, the same reasoning would set an upper bound to its claims, but a political negotiation would eventually decide the final settlement. That settlement would probably take explicit account of elements not introduced here — like pension rights, public property or access to public goods, which might not be properly reflected in the receipts and expenditures considered here. More importantly still, the stationarily hypotheses used here might be questioned, and replaced by explicit anticipations about likely future developments. And the prospect of a settlement less favourable to the relatively poor region that suggested by the formulae of this section would hinder the prospects for a Pareto-improving reorganization. That sobering conclusion must probably be accepted as a fact of life.

9.4.5 Numerical example

By way of illustration I have applied the formulae developed elsewhere (Drèze 1993b, Appendix B) to available Belgian data. Belgium is an interesting, but extreme example due to its very high debt-GDP ratio. There exist estimates of regionalised public receipts, public expenditures and GDP for a few years up to 1985; see Van Rompuy and Bilsen (1988). The same data are used by De Grauwe (1991). The key figures for Belgium and Wallonia in 1985 are presented in Table 9.1 where I use the current debt-GDP ratio of 1.3.

An important feature of Table 9.1 is the primary deficit of Wallonia (-4 percent) compared to the primary surplus of Belgium (5 percent). Consequently, formula (1) yields the unreasonable result that, in case of separation, Wallonia should inherit a *negative* share of Belgium's national debt, namely -22 percent.

Even if over the years following 1985, Belgium's debt-GDP ratio was just about sustainable[12] we should include the objective of progressively bringing down the debt-GDP ratio towards the Maastricht reference of 60 percent. Using conservative estimates of the nominal interest (8.5 percent) and growth rate (3.5 percent), the share of Wallonia in Belgium's public debt is assessed at 18 percent if that objective is to be reached within 10 years, at 12 percent for a 15-year target, and at 8 percent if the horizon is set at 20 years.[13] These crude calculations must be regarded as a mere numerical illustration.

Table 9.1 Public finances of Belgium and Wallonia, 1985

		Belgium	Wallonia
Million Belgian Francs			
Public receipts	R	2,225,407	670,855
Public expenditures	E	2,008,735	718,000
Primary balance	R-E	216,672	-47,145
	R+E	4,234,142	1,388,855
GDP	Y	4,364,420	1,163,618
Ratios			
$(R\text{-}E)/GDP = PB/GDP$		0.05	-0.04
$PB_i \,/\, PB_N$			-0.22
$(R_I + E_i)/(R_N + E_N)$			0.33
Relative GDP of Wallonia	$Y_i \,/\, Y_N$		0.27

9.5 OVERALL DESIRABILITY

9.5.1 Tentative comments

The economic discussion in Sections 9.3 and 9.4 barely scratches the surface of the problems involved. Each of the issues raised is more complex than recognized here, and typically calls for substantive information not readily available (for instance, I could not find figures on public expenditures in Corsica, or figures for Belgium beyond 1985). Hopefully, we can now see how each specific issue fits into a broader picture, and what aspects of the issue seem to matter.

To illustrate this last point, consider the problem of what to do about the assets (like state forests) and liabilities (like state pensions) of a central government in case a region secedes. A first answer is that, if the receipts and expenditures of the state forest, or the contributions and payments pertaining to state pensions, are included in the accounting over a suitable horizon, then no further adjustment is called for. A second answer is that whatever special treatment is proposed should be fitted into the global logic of Section 9.4, as part of an overall settlement guided by overall principles, rather than being decided piecemeal.

Superficial as it is, my economic discussion serves the modest purpose of this paper in two ways. First, it illustrates the kind of professional analysis that will be required in every sphere (legal, political, administrative, ...) if the concept of SRE is to be investigated systematically. Second, it throws some (faint) light on the interaction between the SRE and the process of European integration.

As explained at the outset, this chapter does not claim that the merits of an SRE outweigh the drawbacks, it only claims that the potential merits invite further investigation. The discussion of some economic aspects has led me to recognize the need for further information and research on the real costs and benefits of regional autonomy. It has led me to suggest that a criterion of distributive neutrality could probably forestall the risks of destabilizing national entities — but also to recognize that application of the criterion in practical instances might be controversial. And it has led me to raise an issue of stabilizing coinsurance, which remains to be investigated more systematically. Hopefully, my discussion may spur further work on these issues, which are far from settled.

I would imagine that the intricacy of the issues arising in other areas will be comparable. Thus, the idea of a European citizenship not derived from citizenship in a member state is bound to raise a host of legal questions, that specialists should investigate. In the process, they are apt to encounter problems requiring new research. And the same applies to all areas. My economic discussion illustrates well the need for a timely investigation of these issues by specialists of the relevant disciplines. Such investigations should also prove instructive regarding the process of European integration. As mentioned at the outset, I regard as feasible, and worth discussing, the prospect of fitting the 'Status of Region of Europe' into the existing architecture of our 'Europe of Nations'. I do not regard the SRE as a step towards a 'Europe of Regions'.

Still some of the issues discussed here bear on the relative merits of the two approaches to European integration, or on desirable features of either. To illustrate, consider again the issue of mutual insurance. I have explained in Section 9.3.3 why an autonomous region, deciding on its own taxes and transfers (in particular, its social security system), might find it difficult to enter into a mutual insurance arrangement with other regions, or with the rest of the EC. There is a moral hazard problem. The nations of Europe have until now shied away from mutual insurance of macroeconomic shocks, and in particular from any form of European social security integration. That reluctance is partly due to a confusion between the redistributive aspect and the insurance aspect. Any confusion aside, the reluctance is entertained by the moral hazard aspect. Taking that reluctance into account, I would personally recommend leaving any dimension of mutual insurance out of the SRE, at this stage.

Yet, I have also argued that the moral hazard problem should not necessarily lead to rejection of mutual insurance. Rather, one should try to ascertain a second-best partial insurance. If that could be done, the analysis would apply to the Nations of Europe as well as to the Regions of Europe (and to the internal organization of federal nations). And if, at some stage (which I do not now foresee, honestly), a partial insurance mechanism were developed among Regions of Europe, this might influence our thinking about mutual insurance at the European level. More generally, if a minimal set of public functions were carried out by the EC on behalf of Regions of Europe, this might pave the way for availability of the same functions to all citizens of Europe. It might either accelerate or slow down any transition from a Europe of Nations towards a Europe of Regions. On the one hand, the existence of an SRE might facilitate the transition. On the other hand, it might reduce the pressure towards such a transition, since the SRE could be used by those most eager to operate as a Region of Europe rather than as a region within a national member state.

9.5.2 Regional autonomy

Does the SRE offer opportunities that go beyond those consistent with added autonomy within existing nations? My tentative answer is that it makes little difference, on logical grounds, whether a region operates under the SRE, or achieves *exactly the same degree of autonomy* within an existing nation.

The clearest differences would concern the public functions carried out at the central level. For instance, it could make some difference to Corsica whether its currency is the French franc or the ECU, whether its citizens serve in the French army or participate in defence activities of the WEU, etc. But the major issues lie probably elsewhere. How much regional autonomy can realistically be achieved within a national state? To what extent are regional aspirations to autonomy a form of rejection of national appurtenance? On both counts, enlarging the range of available alternatives offers the prospect of Pareto-improvement.

NOTES AND REFERENCES

1. At least one historical precedent can be mentioned, namely the Holy Roman-Germanic Empire which existed for several centuries (962-1648) with mixed fortunes and mixed membership, combining nations and regions directly attached to the Empire.
2. See Buchanan (1990) for an incisive discussion of some aspects of external federalism.
3. See, e.g. Walters (1987)
4. In this paragraph, I have attempted to define the interregional aspect of the stabilizing function through mutual insurance aginst region-specific shocks. This departs from the standard view which describes the stabilizing function as exercised through policies aimed at dampening macroeconomic fluctuations, and which would treat risk-sharing as an allocative activity. The reason for the more specific definition is of course that I am trying to isolate functions, the exercise of which would be affected by seccession. Policies that involve neither interregional redistributions nor interegional insurance, but rather symmetrical reactions to symmetrical shocks, would not, in principle, be affected by secession: they could continue to be implemented region by region (There does, however, arise a coordination issue - not taken up here.) Interregional risk-sharing would definitely be affected.

5. In France, university professors of economics are recruited through a national competition, and 'winners' choose among the available jobs in the order given by their ranking in the competition.
6. *A contrario*, one might point to free-riding by a country like Luxembourg, whose students attend the public universities of neigbouring countries, at tuition fees well below marginal costs.
7. By partial insurance I mean proportional insurance coverage - *not* full mutual insurance of part of the risks. The closest analogy to the problem of defining an efficient compromise comes from the literature on agency or principal-agent problems in Drèze 1993b, i.e. in Appendix A. A broader viewpoint would link the extent of partial insurance to the departure of regional standards from national standards.
8. I once tried - unsuccessfully - to promote the much simpler idea that Belgium, as an oil importer, and Norway, as an oil exporter, could benefit from a long-term mutual insurance contract on oil prices.
9. All results are formally derived in Drèze 1993b, i.e. in Appendix B, which is self-contained at the cost of some repetition).
10. A progressive scheme would instead impose a higher percentage adjustment in that area where per capita income is higher.
11. Appendix B in Drèze (1993b) proposes a sharing rule which prescribes that the debt-GDP ratio must be reduced to a given target level at a certain date.
12. This follows from formula (B11) in Appendix B of Drèze, 1993b). For $PB_N/Y_N = 0.05$ and $D_N/Y_N = 1.3$, the value of , g solving equation (B11) is 0.05/1.3 = 0.038, which is about right. At today's figures of $PB_N/Y_N = 0.043$ and $r = 0.083$, g would have to be as high as 0.05 in order for sustainability to hold.
13. The corresponding values for the coefficient gamma of budgetary adjustment are 0.12 for $T = 10$, 0.05 for $T = 15$ and 0.04 for $T = 20$, suggesting that $T = 15$, gamma = 0.05 and $D_i/D - N = 0.12$ provide an interesting (even if politically explosive) reference. (See Appendix B in Drèze, 1993b).

BIBLIOGRAPHY

ARROW, K.J. (1963) 'Uncertainty and the Welfare Economics of Medical Care', *American Economic Review*.

BEWLEY, T.F. (1981) 'A Critique of Tiebout's Theory of Local Public Expenditures', *Econometrica.*

BORCH, K. (1962) 'Equilibrium in a Reinsurance Market', *Econometrica.*

BUCHANAN, J.M. (1990) 'Europe's Constitutional Opportunity', in G. Mather (ed.), *Europe's Constitutional Future*, Institute of Economic Affairs, London.

CASELLA, A. and B. FREY (1992) 'Federalism and Clubs: Towards an Economic Theory of Overlapping Political Jurisdictions', *European Economic Review.*

DE GRAUWE, P. (1991) 'Denkoefeningen over de Regionalisering van de Belgische Overheidsschuld', *Leuvense Economische Standpunten.*

DREZE, J.H. (1990) 'The Role of Securities and Labor Contracts in the Optimal Allocation of Risk-Bearing', in H. Louberg (ed.), *Risk, Information and Insurance, Essays in the Memory of Karl H. Borch*, Kluwer Academic Publishers, Boston; also reprinted as Chap. 11 in J.H. Drèze, *Underemployment Equilibria; Essays in Theory, Econometrics and Policy*, (1990).

DREZE, J.H. (1993a) 'Can Varying Social Insurance Contributions Improve Labour Market Efficiency?', forthcoming in *The Economics of Partnership: A Third Way?*, A.B. Atkinson, ed., Macmillan, London.

DREZE, J.H. (1993b) 'Regions of Europe: a feasible status, to be discussed', *Economic Policy*, April, p. 266-307.

DREZE, J.H. and C. COLLIER (1993) 'Risk-Sharing on the Labour Market and Second-Best Wage Rigidities', *European Economic Review.*

HOLMSTRÖM, B. (1982) 'Moral Hazard in Teams', *The Bell Journal of Economics.*

MUSGRAVE, R. (1959) *The Theory of Public Finance*, McGraw-Hill, New York.

OATES, W.E. (1972) *Fiscal Federalism*, Harcourt Brace Jovanovich, New York.

VAN ROMPUY, P. and . V. BILSEN (1988) 'Tien jaar Financiële Stromen tussen de Gewesten in België', *Leuvense Economische Standpunten.*

WALTERS, A. (1987) 'Currency Boards', in *The New Palgrave*, J. Eatwell, M. Milgate and P. Newman (eds) Macmillan, London.

10 Central and Eastern European Economies in Transition: The Contribution of the Bretton Woods Institutions

Bernard Snoy

10.1 INTRODUCTION

A whole region — from Central Europe to Central Asia — has embarked on a path of transformation the extent of which has few parallels in history. Following the historic collapse of party-state domination of their societies and their economies, countries in Central and Eastern Europe (CEE) and the Former Soviet Union (FSU) face two daunting challenges: to move from centrally planned towards competitive market economies, and at the same time to maintain and strengthen newly gained democracies. The road is perilous — both economically and politically — and largely untrodden, although many of the individual elements of reform have been confronted before in other countries. Still fragile political systems must address the challenges of complex economic and institutional reforms in an external environment more difficult than originally envisaged and, in some cases, in the midst of rising ethnic and regional tensions. Widespread initial euphoria after political transitions in 1989 and 1991 has been replaced by a more sober assessment of the task ahead.

These momentous events have moved the Bretton Woods institutions, created fifty years ago to underpin monetary cooperation and to promote the economic development of the unified family of nations, closer to the realisation of the dream of their founding fathers. For the first time in their history, the International Monetary Fund (IMF) and the IBRD (International Bank for Reconstruction and Development) — better known as the World Bank — have become genuine global institutions. With membership increasing in a few years from about 150 to 178, they have had to cope, both in quantitative and qualitative terms, with an unprecedented increase in the demand for their financial and advisory services.

This chapter focuses on what we have learned from the early history of the transition process and on the specific contributions to it of the International Monetary Fund and the World Bank Group.

10.2 WHAT HAVE WE LEARNED ABOUT THE SYSTEMIC TRANSFORMATION?

We will concentrate on the three most essential conditions for a successful process of systemic transformation :

- a legal, institutional and human basis of a market economy;
- an early macro-economic stabilisation and — of crucial importance for the success of income policies — tax reform and the design of a well targeted safety net;
- an innovative approach to solve the most difficult and the most central problem of the systemic transformation, i.e. the governance, the restructuring and the privatisation of the major state owned enterprises and the reform of the banks to which they are overindebted.

10.2.1 The legal, institutional and human basis of a market economy

The magnitude of the task of creating the legal, institutional and human basis of a market economy has been generally underestimated. Yet, the hiatus between the collapse of central planning and the establishment of the foundations of a market economy caused the temporary absence of an effective coordinating mechanism. Combined with the collapse of the trade and payments arrangements and the collapse of public expenditures related to the military industrial complex, this hiatus accounts for a large part of the unexpected depth of the transition recession, particularly in the countries which had not experimented with economic reforms before 1989, such as Rumania, Bulgaria, Albania and the republics of the FSU.

The most fundamental building blocs of a market economy are the definition and protection of property rights — including intellectual property — and the unenforceability of contracts, i.e. a framework for exchanging those rights. Without such prerequisites private investment, whether domestic or foreign, will not take place. Company and foreign investment laws are needed to regulate entry into economic activities and define rules of corporate governance. Also lending relationships cannot develop without an adequate legislation on secured transactions, including a system of registration of collateral. Rules of the game for exit, i.e. bankruptcy law, are equally important; without a bankruptcy law, the imposition of financial discipline lacks credibility. Nothing is worse than granting freedom to enterprises without mechanisms to impose financial discipline: the result is high inflation, capital flight and irresponsible stripping of assets. Price liberalisation is also likely to result in a huge transfer of resources from consumers to producers in the absence of anti-monopoly and unfair competition laws. These basic areas of laws must be joined by other important ones — such as labour, taxation and banking, to name just those — to make possible the kind of behaviour, in particular the supply response to a stabilisation programme, routinely assumed from economic agents in a market economy.

The establishment of this legal basis needs to be complemented by massive investment in institution building and training. Indeed, legal codes are useless without public and private institutions capable to understand, apply and enforce them. The court system and the government agencies must inspire trust. Public administrations need to be revamped, decentralised and adapted to their new role in a market economy. Institution building is also needed in the private sector on the basis of a modern business legislation and professional organisations, while chambers of commerce and the like have a crucial role to play in the development of a new entrepreneurial culture. Last but not least, a huge effort is needed to train public and private decision makers in the economic, legal, management, financial, marketing and accounting techniques which advanced market economies have had decades or centuries to develop and refine.

The degree of development of the legal institutional and human basis of a market economy is probably the most important discriminating factor. It explains why Poland, the Czech Republic, Hungary and Slovenia — which benefited from pre-World War II (or even pre-World War I) free market industrial antecedents, started earlier with the institutional reforms or implemented them most consistently — are among the transition countries with the best prospects for a sustained resumption of growth. In any case, there appears to be a close correlation between the success of macroeconomic stabilisation programmes and the reforms on the legal and institutional fronts.

Conversely, prospects for sustained non-inflationary economic growth in Russia might be hampered by the delays and difficulties encountered by legal and institutional reforms. The worse manifestation of these weaknesses is the emergence of 'mafias', that is organised crime. As shown by Daniel Yergin and Thane Gustafson (1994) in their provocative book 'Russia 2010', much of the new private business activity in Russia today lies in a grey zone somewhere between legality and illegality, not so much because the business is itself reprehensible, but because the law has not caught up with the new fact of private enterprise.Since no one can say with any certainty what is legal and what is illegal, any deal may require a bribe or at least a friendly official who 'looks through his fingers'. Friendship remains the basis of the Russian economy, just as it was in the Soviet period. The legal and moral twilight zone hinders the development of attitudes that would support a market system. People must have a minimum of trust in one another to do business. There must be confidence that the law will protect contracts and property. If people do not trust the system and their future in it, individuals will not save and business will not invest. Inequalities of income and property will not be tolerated if almost everyone is convinced that gains are ill-gotten. If people's beliefs and behaviour do not support a market system, it will end up developing only in a very truncated way'. One may therefore conclude indeed that the success of the transition process and the stability — both political and economic — of its outcome depends largely on each country's ability to build up rapidly the appropriate legal and institutional framework. This is also a priority task for external sources of assistance, including the Bretton Woods institutions.

10.2.2 Macro-economic stabilisation, incomes policies, tax reform and the safety net

A second fundamental lesson is that macro-economic stabilisation through the control of budgetary and monetary aggregates is a must for a successful transition. Indeed, as in the rest of the world, inflation and macro-economic instability distorts incentives, discourages investment and foreign assistance which risks ending up in capital flight. High inflation endangers the positive developments emerging spontaneously in the private sector and increases the probability of reversals on the policy front.

The earlier debate on the merits of shock therapy versus gradualism has faded, at least in the context of Central Europe. Stabilisation has to be achieved and to be achieved early. But the real problem is how to create as quickly as possible the institutional conditions for achieving stabilisation and, once it has been achieved, how to sustain a non-inflationary course. Besides the legal and institutional factors mentioned above, the three areas which are crucial for the success of the stabilisation programmes are incomes policies, tax reform and the establishment of better targeted safety nets.

a. Incomes policies

In addition to dealing with the monetary overhang when prices are liberalised, transition economies are faced with a specific danger for macro economic destabilisation. It stems from a lack of countervailing power to workers and managers and more generally from an absence of financial discipline in enterprises until they can be privatised. This explains the crucial role of incomes policies during the transition.

Indeed, as shown by Fabrizio Coricelli and Ana Revenga (1992) in the Polish case, decontrol of prices and subsidy removal are bound to trigger extremely large pressures for compensatory wage increases thus undermining the process of stabilising the economy. Coming from a 'full employment' regime, there is no intrinsic moderating force on wages, no perception of a Phillips curve. Furthermore, as workers are confronted with the possibility of privatisation or even commercialisation, they may face the perverse incentive to 'decapitalise' the firms. This means resources needed to maintain the capital stock and to carry out new investments may instead be paid out in higher wages. By substituting for the lack of owners, a wage control policy is assumed to act as a deterrent against both decapitalisation of firms and inflationary spirals of wage pressures. In addition, wage policies may be an effective anchor to strengthen the credibility of governments and guarantee the sustainability of exchange rate and/or monetary anchors.

However, wage policy cannot be used as a substitute for resolving the ownership issue for a longer period. More generally, wage policies cannot be sustained if workers and managers of state-owned enterprises perceive that the government will be unwilling or unable to impose a hard-budget constraint on the firm. Lack of financial discipline in enterprises, particularly through accumulation of inter-enterprise arrears, has been indeed the Achilles heel in the stabilisation programmes of a number of countries in transition, particularly Russia and other republics of the FSU. McKinnon (1994) has shown that, as long as the old socialist distinction is retained between enterprises, which are not cash constrained in their ability to bid for scarce resources, and cash-constrained households, decontrol of all producer prices instead of solving the cash overhang problem, will only launch a new inflationary spiral. In addition to regaining control over money and credit, the retaining of some price controls on soft-budget state enterprises may be a necessary second best solution, at least in the short term.

b. Fiscal reform

Another threat to macro-economic stabilisation during the transition process stems from the collapse of the traditional sources of government revenue, particularly the profits of state owned enterprises. The creation of a new tax system is a particularly urgent task. Taxes in centrally planned economies were relatively rudimentary tools to capture surplus and were applied in a highly discretionary manner. New tax systems, to be based primarily on the value added tax and the individual and corporate income taxes, need to be transparent, predictable and well enforced. As with other legal systems it is much easier to change tax law than tax administration as methods need to be modernised in order to deal with hundreds of thousands of private firms and individuals. This requires, among others, techniques of selective auditing and tax enforcement, standard accounting practices and a reliable and objective legal framework for dispute resolution. In the early years of the transition, it is particularly difficult to get the emerging private sector to contribute its fair share in the tax revenue.

c. The social safety net and social services

The establishment of social safety nets where they do not exist yet (e.g. in Russia) and their reorientation and streamlining where they do exist (e.g. in Central Europe) are indispensable to ensure the socio-political sustainability of the stabilisation programmes. It is also a prerequisite for the enforcement of hard budget constraints on enterprises, their privatisation and their restructuring in countries such as Russia, where enterprises were the main providers of social services to their workers and their families. Besides welfare services to address poverty directly, such safety nets should include unemployment benefits of limited duration and retraining services and be combined with complete overhauls of pensions disability insurance as well as of the delivery and financing of health care and other social services. The limited budgetary resources available for better targeted safety nets could be combined with mass privatisation programmes providing citizens as well as pension funds with real assets. Such assets could be used as collateral in bad times. Privatisation of the housing stock would furthermore allow underemployed workers to minimise the opportunity cost of underemployment.

10.2.3 Privatisation restructuring, financial sector reform and enterprise governance

Whereas the freeing of entry for new enterprises and the privatisation of small business are relatively easy, the most difficult task is the restructuring and privatisation of large enterprises. Together with financial reform, this really constitutes the hard-core of the transformation process, where the strongest vested interests are also entrenched.

Most countries have developed parallel tracks of privatisation: (i) a fast track for small and medium-size enterprises — particularly in services — to be based on auctions and for large enterprises a combination of classical case by case privatisation, involving whenever possible a strategic investor, and (ii) 'mass privatisation', including the issuance of vouchers and special incentives for managers and workers. Yet, privatisation along these two tracks has generally been slower than expected. On the one hand, political resistance to large enterprise privatisation tends to increase as time goes by, and, on the other hand, investor interest may be discouraged by concessions made to workers and other stakeholders.

Furthermore, privatisation cannot be separated from three almost intractable problems: corporate governance in the interim period, restructuring and overindebtedness:

- First, as privatisation of large enterprises takes time, there is a major problem of governance in the interim period, as managers' and workers' interests do not coincide with those of the enterprise. The quality of governance in the transition period deteriorates markedly when enterprises remain 'in limbo'. They must either have a clear privatisation plan with firm deadlines or they should remain in the public sector subject to strict tests of accountability and performance. Most of the Central European countries have set up state holding companies or funds to solve this governance problem.
- Second, it is difficult to privatise loss making enterprises. Restructuring is the solution but it requires human and financial resources which are generally lacking. Imaginative solutions supported by foreign technical assistance are needed. 'Unbundling' of assets has a role to play in this connection. Because new private firms will be facing scarce credits, it is crucial that — either through privatisation or restructuring — as many 'unbundled' assets as possible are released into the market. This is particularly relevant for the conversion to civilian production of defence-related enterprises, the excess capacity of which can be used as a source of equipment for the new private industries.
- Third, overindebtedness is another obstacle to privatisation. It is part of the more global problem of lack of financial discipline and of the perverse relations that have been allowed to develop between overindebted state owned enterprises and their banks, whose balance sheets are poisoned by bad loans.

More generally the development of a sound and efficient financial sector capable of mobilising savings and allocating credit is not possible without addressing these problems. The banks themselves have to be privatised or, when it is not possible, their governance must be improved with increased incentives to enforce financial discipline on their debtors.

But there is also a danger of premature foreclosure and bankruptcy, particularly when the present inability to service past debt is not an indicator of potential profitability. Assistance is needed to help these banks develop the technical capacity to participate in enterprise restructuring, recapitalisation and debt equity swaps. In some cases, the problems are so intractable, e.g. for enterprises which account for the bulk of employment in a particular city, that a selective government intervention may be needed together with strictly limited budget subsidies to facilitate more gradual restructuring and phasing out of enterprises with important social externalities.

10.3 THE CONTRIBUTION OF THE INTERNATIONAL MONETARY FUND

The Bretton Woods institutions were caught unprepared by the historical events which took place since 1989 and by the scale and complexity of the task of assisting systemic transformation, particularly in the republics of the former Soviet Union. Membership increased by more than 20 and staff resources had to be redirected to meet the new challenge. Poland was the first country of the region to adopt in 1990 a bold and comprehensive stabilisation programme supported by an IMF standby facility. By the end of 1992, standby arrangements had been negotiated with each of the Central European countries (with the exception of the successor states of the former Yugoslavia), the Baltic States and Russia. Hungary benefited also from an Extended Fund Facility (EFF) Arrangement and Albania was able to draw in 1993 from the Enhanced Structural Adjustment Facility (ESAF). New standby arrangements were negotiated in 1993 with Kazakhstan, Kyrgyzstan and Moldova.

In view of the enormous problems confronting Russia and the other states of the FSU, as well as other economies in transition, the IMF created in April 1993 a new temporary facility, the Systemic Transformation Facility (STF). The STF is specially designed to extend financial assistance to members experiencing severe disruptions in their traditional trade and payments arrangements due to a shift from a significant reliance on trading at non market prices to multilateral, market-based trade (particularly for energy products). The STF is tailored to the needs of members which are at an early stage of the transition process and are not able yet to formulate a programme that could be supported by the Fund under its existing facilities and policies. Financing under the STF is provided in two equal purchases. The first half of the total financing is disbursed at the outset. The remainder is normally disbursed in about 6 months but no later than 12 months, after the first purchase, depending, inter alia, on satisfactory progress towards agreement on an upper credit standby, extended on ESAF arrangement. Access is limited to no more than 50 percent of the quota and can be in addition to any financing obtained under other fund facilities. The repayment terms of four and a half to ten years are the same as for financing under the EFF.

To qualify for STF funds, transition countries have to demonstrate that they are liberalising their economies as well as meeting specific macro-economic criteria. For the second tranche of the Russian STF, e.g. this meant an agreement to bring inflation down to 7 per cent a month in 1994 and to keep the budget deficit under 10 per cent of GNP. So far no less than eight FSU countries (Russia, Belarus, Estonia, Latvia, Lithuania, Kazakhstan, Kyrgyzstan and Moldova) as well as Bulgaria, Slovakia and the former Yugoslav Republic of Macedonia have concluded STF arrangements with the Fund. The STF arrangements for Kyrgyzstan, Moldova and Kazakhstan paved the way for subsequent standby arrangements. For all three Baltic republics, the STF is supporting second standby arrangements.

In assessing the performance of the IMF in supporting the transition process, three main questions must be addressed:

1. Have the IMF supported programmes been adequately designed?
2. Has Fund conditionality been too tough or too soft?
3. Has the IMF ensured an adequate external financing of the stabilisation programmes?

10.3.1 Adequacy of the IMF programmes

As regards the first question, the IMF has been confronted with a recurrent criticism, echoing that addressed to its programmes in developing countries, namely that it concentrates too much on the short term requirements of macro-economic stabilisation and that it overlooks the fact that the structural reforms necessary to achieve a stable macro-economic balance have a much longer maturation period. The general argument is that tight focus on short term macro-economic variables has made the fund 'rather blind to institutional issues and theories contained in public choice theory, the property rights school and new institutionalism'. (Mizsei, 1994).

This criticism has some validity but should not be exaggerated as the IMF is putting more and more emphasis on legal and structural reforms. It is true that such reforms take more time, but as demonstrated by Balcerowicz (1993), this is not a reason to postpone urgent measures to regain control of money supply and reduce budget deficits. As shown by Bruno (1992) a distinction must be made between on the one hand price stabilisation for which a gradual solution would lack credibility and would be doomed to failure and import and on the other hand payments liberalisation for which it might be argued that a more gradual approach could mitigate output losses and give enterprises more time to adjust. Besides its traditional expertise in monetary and exchange rate policies, the Fund is increasingly integrating the three above mentioned areas as most important for the success of stabilisation programmes, namely incomes policies, tax reform and safety nets. Furthermore, structural reforms have been more the area of expertise of the World Bank which has provided significant technical and financial assistance supporting such reforms (see further).

According to Gros (1994), the Fund underestimated inflation in Russia following price liberalisation in 1991–92. A more thoughtful estimation of the monetary overhang and greater attention to the inflationary impact of lack of discipline at the enterprise level (see above) would have allowed to forecast the ensuing hyper-inflation.

The Fund also reversed itself on the issue of the creation of separate currencies in the countries of the FSU: first it advised countries in the rouble zone to stay in rather than opt out, hoping that stabilisation of the rouble would benefit them. As stabilisation of the rouble failed, the Fund made introduction of national currencies a condition for its assistance. Many of these new currencies had to be introduced under extremely difficult balance of payments conditions and without sufficient preparation, however.

The controversy is still raging on about whether the Fund was right or not in discarding the option of a payments union. Although proposals for such a union have been rightly perceived by the Visegrad countries as a step backwards, perpetuating the burden of highly inefficient foreign trade transactions (Drabek, 1972), a payments union among the FSU countries appears to be an appealing solution given the extreme degree of specialisation of industry in the former Soviet Union (Bofinger and Gros, 1992). The IMF (1994) does not reject a clearing union among the CIS countries, which would be supported by the proposed Interstate Bank, but it opposes a payments union involving the provision of sizeable amounts of credit from external sources. The IMF's opposition is based on the ground that it could well lead member states to focus their energies on expanding mutual trade at the expense of commerce with the rest of the world at world market prices and could serve as a disincentive for the pursuit of stabilisation policies, delaying the time at which member states' currencies would be made convertible. It could lead to the creation of a new bureaucracy that — given the tradition of central planning in most states of the region, and the continuing reliance on intergovernmental trade agreements and state orders in some countries — could materially slow the progress toward decentralised market relations in interstate trade. More profoundly, the IMF concern appears to be that such bureaucracy, which would become a forum of intense bargaining over the amounts and terms of credit, might become a rival to the IMF itself in the formulation and enforcement of conditionality. Despite its obvious geopolitical dimension, it seems that the proposal for a payments union among the CIS countries deserves further consideration.

10.3.2 Adequacy of conditionality

As concerns the question of conditionality, criticism of the Fund by Sachs (1994) and others has concentrated on the Fund's attitude towards Russia. As explained by Kiekens (1994), there are two views of this issue. The first one holds that it is wrong in principle to link assistance being provided to Russia by the IMF and other international financial institutions with progress in macro-economic stabilisation. Successful stabilisation should be regarded as a result and not as a precondition for external assistance. The second view holds that providing external assistance to a country suffering from financial instability, without first obtaining a firm commitment to macro-economic stabilisation, cannot assist progress with economic reforms. Such unconditional assistance could even result in additional costs to the recipient country both by delaying an inevitable adjustment and by increasing the country's debt burden.

The Fund's position has so far been closest to the second view, i.e. that first indications of successful stabilisation are necessary before the beneficial effects of external assistance can materialise. However, there has also been considerable flexibility in the Fund's approach to Russia. On several occasions when financial assistance was to be released, Russia was given the benefit of the doubt. In fact the STF has become the Fund's flexible response to the new challenges it is facing in the FSU countries as it developed into an important tool for relieving the burden of adjustment in this region. As expressed by Mizsei (1994), 'it has permitted the flow of funds to start to transform economies in the early stages of institutional reform while protecting the integrity and 'market value' of a full IMF standby programme. It sends a positive signal to the market about the country and about the Fund'.

In a recent article, Business Europe (1994) used another convincing argument, namely that the strongest case for tough IMF conditionality in Eastern Europe is that, if the Fund considerably softens up its conditionality, 'the rest of the financial world would have to look elsewhere for its stamp of approval'. Rather than opening up a flood of private financing, a weak programme might scare it away (Mizsei, 1994). Furthermore developing countries would justifiably be worried if more lenient standards were applied to Russia than to them. Discipline would be undermined everywhere. The Fund's loss of credibility would impair its ability to catalyse other assistance, even for countries with strong programmes.

10.3.3 Adequacy of external financing

The third question, namely the adequacy of external financing of economic adjustment by the transition countries is the most difficult one. Experience of the last few years shows that the need for orderly adjustment and an early introduction of currency convertibility required much more resources than the international financial institutions could provide. Their financing had therefore to be supplemented: the composition and the adequacy of these additional financing have been different for Central and Eastern Europe and the Baltic Countries, for Russia and for the other CIS states.

As shown in Table 10.1, for Central and Eastern Europe and the Baltic countries, financing by the international financial institutions was complemented by lending by the OECD countries in the context of the Group of Twenty-Four (G-24) framework, coordinated by the Commission of the European Union. At US$11.6 billion, an amount equivalent to 3% of the estimated combined GNP of these countries, official lending remained below the original assumptions. Private capital flowed in amounts exceeding substantially the expectations and debt relief provided by private and official creditors of Poland and Bulgaria was generous, however. The Bretton Woods institutions definitely achieved their catalytic role. As stabilisation takes hold and the economies of these countries expand, it is anticipated that the high rates of investment required to complete the economic transformation will progressively be financed from private external sources and from increased domestic saving.

Table 10.1 Central European and Baltic countries. External financing, 1991–93[1] (In billions of U.S. dollars)

	Original assumptions	Actual financing	Actual as percent of original[2]
Official lending	15.8	11.6	73
IMF	6.6	5.1	77
World Bank	4.2	2.9	69
Other international institutions	1.3	0.7	54
G-24 countries[3]	3.7	2.9	78
Private capital	14.2	17.4	122
Other[4]	11.1	12.4	117
Total financing	41.1	41.4	101

Source: IMF (1994b)

1 Data for 1993 are provisional. Figures are based on programme years: calendar years for Bulgaria, former Czechoslovakia, Hungary, Poland, Romania and the Baltic states; July 1993-June 1994 for Albania. Poland is not included in 1992, when no annual programme was agreed.

2 For official lending, actual outlays were less high than originally assumed, because of delays in programme implementation due to administrative difficulties and slippages in adjustment efforts.

3 The bulk of the G-24 assistance has been provided by the European Union.

4 Mainly debt relief by private and official creditors for Bulgaria and Poland.

Table 10.2 Russia: Official financial assistance (In billions of U.S. dollars)

	1992		1993		Total[1]	
	Announced	Actual	Announced	Actual	Announced	Actual
Bilateral creditors and European Union[2]	11	14	10	6	21	20[3]
Conditional IMF financing						
IMF facilities	3	1	7	1,5	8	2,5
IMF stabilization fund[4]	6	...	6	...	6	...
World Bank and European Bank for Reconstruction and Development	1,5	...	5	0,5	5	0,5
Official debt relief	2,5[5]	...	15	15[6]	15	15
Total	24	15	43	23	55	38

Source: Russian Federation Ministry of Finance: Vneshekonombank; US Administration press release of April 2, 1992; Chairman's statement of the G-7 Joint Ministerial Meeting and the Following Meeting with the Russian Ministers of April 15, 1993; Tokyo Summmit Economic Declaration of July 9, 1993; and IMF staff estimates.

1 Excludes most double counting (that is, amounts announced but not disbursed in 1992 and announced again in 1993), A small amount of double counting n the two-year total may nevertheless persist.
2 Does not include grants from Germany of more than $3 billion to rehouse Russian troops.
3 Excludes some items in the announced packages for which reliable data are not available (technical assistance, nuclear facility rehabilitation, and the like).
4 The 56 billion stabilization fund was potentially available in both 1992 and 1993 to help stabilize the rouble in the context of a comprehensive reform strategy. It was not activated because the appropriate conditions were notin place.
5 This amount was not formally granted during 1992.
6 Includes $6,(billion deferred or in arrears in 1992.

Among the countries of the former Soviet Union, Russia emerges as a privileged case. To alleviate the impact of the transition process. Russia received official external financing in 1992 and 1993 totalling almost $38 billion (Table 10.2). In addition, Germany provided grants of more than $3 billion, and there was a further $16 billion in commercial debt-service deferral. Official financing was conditional on the implementation of appropriate macro-economic stabilisation policies, and much of the difference between announced amounts and those actually disbursed — some $17 billion over the two years— Table 10.2 is related to failure to put these policies in place. A new agreement providing for the rescheduling of $24 billion of Russian debt owed to commercial banks was reached in October 1994. It should not be forgotten also that Russia has suffered from massive capital flight in recent years and that the pool of foreign assets held by Russians abroad could, as it was earlier the case in some Latin American countries, provide a very significant source of financing for economic reconstruction once macro-economic stability has been reestablished.

To an even greater extent than had been the case in Central and Eastern Europe, most of the other CIS countries have experienced a steep decline in the large explicit and implicit transfers that had been received from Russia. These included fiscal transfers from the former Union budget, which disappeared in 1992, and the subsidy implicit in the underpricing of energy and raw material exports, relative to world prices, which was reduced significantly as interstate prices for these goods were raised. Between 1992 and 1994, the loss of official transfers from Russia and the rise in the import bill — on the assumption that energy and materials prices rise to world levels — may cost the countries of the former Soviet Union other than Russia $15 billion, or about 15 per cent of their estimated 1994 GDP.

It is also in this context that one should see the proposals of supplementing existing reserve assets in the world with a new allocation of SDR 36 billion. Further to a rechannelling mechanism, these additional reserves could be directly and exclusively used to complement the conditional financing already provided by the IMF through the STF to the transition countries and through ESAF to low-income countries. One of the arguments to make the transition countries benefit particularly from this SDR allocations is that almost none of these countries participated in previous SDR allocations since they were not yet members of the Fund when these allocations took place.

10.4 THE CONTRIBUTION OF THE WORLD BANK GROUP

For the World Bank Group (i.e. the World Bank together with the International Development Association — IDA — and the International Finance Institution — IFC) as for the IMF, the challenge of systemic transformation and the entry of more than 20 new members generated a profound reallocation of human resources, to some extent, at the expense of the Bank's traditional clients, the developing countries. Whereas IMF technical and financial assistance was primarily aimed to support stabilisation, the Bank Group's areas of comparative advantage are in structural and sectoral reforms and investment lending. Although it took some time to formulate specific country strategies and there were difficulties and discontinuities in their implementation, the Bank Group worked out an agenda in support of systemic transformation including the following:

a. rehabilitation loans as a first way to support wholesale reforms and finance critically needed imports in order to stop the deflationary spiral;
b. increasing emphasis on enterprise restructuring and privatisation as an increasingly central issue for the systemic transformation;
c. establishing safety nets and new labour policies as part of an overhaul of social policies;
d. supporting key sectors particularly infrastructure, energy, agriculture, and the environment; and
e. coordinating international assistance, especially in the area of technical assistance.

10.4.1 Rehabilitation and institution building loans

Before moving to traditional investment loans, the Bank used the instrument of its policy-based loans, introduced since 1980 for developing countries under the name of structural adjustment loans, to support wholesale institutional reforms or at least the first steps of such reforms. The Bank moved much faster than in any other region to these comprehensive and quick-disbursing adjustment operations without having — except in Hungary — the benefit of the knowledge gained in years of project interventions. Very quickly the Bank set up structural adjustment loans (SALs) for Poland, Hungary, the former Czechoslovakia, Bulgaria and Romania. The initial orientation given in 1992 for the countries of the former Soviet Union was to prepare rehabilitation loans, i.e. adjustment operations supporting the initial thrust of wholesale change in the economic policy framework and financing critically needed imports. An equally crucial instrument was institution building operations to help develop the market institutions to support the new set of policies. None of this would have been possible without considerable investment in analytical studies, i.e. country economic memoranda, including fairly advanced sectoral analyses. These reports provided the basis for strategic country discussions with the economic managers of these countries and the organisation of consultative group meetings would not have been feasible without them.

Since the introduction by the IMF of the Systemic Transformation Facility in April 1993, the Bank's emphasis changed for the following reasons:

- First of all the psychological climate had changed. The euphoria was over. The painful daily management of the transformation had replaced the enthusiasm of tearing down walls. People wanted the system changed essentially because they wanted a better life. What they saw, however, was a tremendous compression in output since the beginning of the transition process.
- Second, the Bank took conscience of the extraordinary rigidities inherited from the previous system. In fact much of the former system was still in existence in the physical configuration of the capital stock and the organisation of the enterprises. The difficulties and the institutional requirements to introduce and to strengthen completion, especially in the former Soviet Union, had clearly been underestimated.
- Third, the Bank began to understand better the constraints — resulting particularly in FSU countries — from the weakness and very slow build up of the lateral purchasing and selling relations among enterprises to replace the central orders that had been the backbone of the previous system. Ninety per cent of what in 1994 was foreign trade across borders in the new nation states of the former Soviet Union originally was domestic trade within the former Soviet Union. New reliable forms of trade and payments have yet to

emerge.

• Fourth, the massive shift in demand was underestimated. The loss of guaranteed orders, particularly for heavy industry in military-related production, which originally accounted for almost half of GDP in some countries, had a dramatic impact on enterprises. The implication was that the physical stock of capital plants and equipments, were to a large extent locked into units without customers. The tragedy was that these countries had, for two generations, realised investment rates that were among the highest in the world, with all the attendant foregoing of consumption. Past savings were be blocked as a result of over-industrialisation.

Implicit in the above causes for the decline of output was a new Bank agenda for action, facing more squarely the central issue of enterprise adaptation, namely, what was to be done with the existing capital stock.

10.4.2 Loans supporting enterprise and financial reform

The above view led to a new philosophy, i.e. that obviously some part of the capital stock and of the existing organisation constituted a potential. Not only is there a lot of technical sophistication, also managers and well trained workers represent important human capital. What is missing are market institutions. It is necessary to move away from the dominating 'production mentality' and the excessive confidence that new investment in the existing structures will solve all problems. The central questions are what kind of enterprise governance — a broad concept which goes beyond privatisation — is needed to create adaptation? In what way can the banking system to which enterprises are highly indebted be an instrument for that reform? What kind of strategic interventions by the authorities, backed up by the World Bank and other agencies, can catalyze the necessary restructurings?

The central thesis of the new emerging World Bank strategy is that financial sector reform, enterprise restructuring and enterprise governance, including privatisation, are inextricable entwined and must be handled in concert. It was only in 1993 that this new approach had sufficiently matured to make possible, a project in Poland that dealt concurrently with the three issues and for which a $450 million loan was approved by the Bank in 1993.

Crucial in this new approach are both the recapitalisation of the commercial banks and the reinforcement of their institutional capacities, in order to allow them to influence where the adaptation of debtor enterprises should lead, where product lines need to be changed and where credit has to be denied. This is based on 'work out' plans for sectors and for enterprises, including techniques of debt restructuring and debt/equity conversion. At the same time, the new approach avoids to overburden the commercial banks by asking them to handle the problems they could not cope with because they involve socially significant problems such as entire towns depending on particular enterprises. A crucial piece of the approach is a 'government intervention fund' with clear rules for restructuring sale or liquidation of enterprises that the commercial banks cannot handle. To prevent the temptation of a bail out by the intervention fund, a powerful incentive is created for the commercial banks to call on this fund only in the last resort i.e. that the claims of the 'intervention fund' on any enterprise will always come before those of the commercial banks.

The World Bank has been active in working out sectoral plans to deal with threatened industries — for instance coal and steel — in collaboration with the trade unions and are aimed at privatisation at the end of the road. A number of donors have agreed to convert part of their contribution to Poland's stabilisation fund in cofinancing. Operations of this kind are the strategic focus of World Bank lending in other countries as well. In Russia, the Bank has been able to mount three operations with similar objectives: the Russia Enterprise Restructuring Project supports initiation of term lending to private enterprises by a core of commercial banks, while another project is providing for institutional strengthening and systems modernisation for these banks. A third project supports privatisation with massive assistance in design, in implementation capacity up to the local level and in information campaigns.

The IFC has also been extremely active in this field, concentrating its assistance on the execution of public auctions for small and medium enterprises and other privatisation transactions with a significant demonstration effect (e.g. in Nizhny Novgorod, in the area of Volgograde and in Tomsk). These activities have not created little islands but have generated a thrust towards replicability. Privatisation is also an area where the cooperation between the World Bank Group, both the IBRD and IFC, with the EBRD (European Bank for Reconstruction and Development) has been exemplary.

10.4.3 Redesigning safety nets and labour policies

While the Bank saw enterprise restructuring and private sector development as the key to recovery in a market setting, it did not neglect the social sectors. The World Bank was conscious that the political feasibility of the reform process could be jeopardised unless a safety net and associated labour policies mitigated the pains of transition.

The Bank's analytical work showed first that in none of the countries was consumption allowed to fall in line with output and that the victim of the contraction was public investment rather than consumption. Secondly, in Central and Eastern Europe, although not in the former Soviet Union, the available starting basis was comparable to what existed in some industrial countries and much better than in most developing countries. Social expenditures — whatever their exact definition — ranged between 30 and 40 per cent of GDP. Quantitatively, there was a certain mass for restructuring. The Bank involved itself very deeply in advising countries in transition in the restructuring of their social protection system, putting emphasis on the establishment of a realistic poverty line, the tightening of eligibility for social benefits and the reduction of some forms of support from salary-based to flat rates. Conscious that social sector issues went beyond establishing safety nets, the Bank got involved in the reform of support services, unemployment registration, retraining and placement services, areas which required significant investments in physical and human capital to face the challenge of transition. The Bank loans for Hungary approved in 1993 supporting a pensions administration and health insurance project and an health services and management project represent the most advanced effort to restructure the social sectors in a transition economy, which could pave the way to similar operations in the rest of the region. The World Bank established a regional mission in Budapest responsible exclusively for the preparation and supervision of social sector projects.

The establishment of an appropriate safety net constitutes an extremely challenging task for the Russian Federation and the other former Soviet Republics. In a special study the World Bank suggests that the existing mechanisms of social protection are deeply inadequate to protect the most vulnerable groups of the Russian society in the ongoing transition, in particular pensioners, single parent families, families with more than two children and disabled persons. About 50 million Russians out of 149 million are now estimated to fall below the poverty line. Even if the existing social safety net, which absorbs about 10 per cent of GDP is restructured, it will be insufficient. Up to five percent equivalent may be required to meet the additional needs. This shift is substantial but feasible if subsidies – explicit or implicit in systems of directed creditor-subsidized exchange rates – which amounted up to 40 per cent of GDP in 1993 are phased down. According to the Bank, the main contribution which should be expected from the outside world is not to finance this shift itself – which in principle does not require foreign exchange – but to finance the technical assistance needed to create the necessary institutional capacities at the federal, regional ('oblast') and municipal levels.

The World Bank has also identified a key problem resulting from the weakening of the Russian Federation and the devolution of responsibility for social programmes to the 'oblast' and municipal levels. This devolution comes at the cost of widening the existing disparities between regions. Given the structure and concentration of industry in Russia, it is likely that the economic base of many localities will collapse. Furthermore, the pressure on local authorities will increase as enterprises withdraw from the provision of local infrastructure and services, which local authorities are being required to take over. Given the absence of a mechanism to redistribute public resources among 'oblast', the Bank has recommended the creation of an Equalisation Fund in a special report about 'intergovernmental fiscal relations in the Russian Federation'.

10.4.4 Support for infrastructure, energy and environmental projects

In infrastructure, the Bank's first aim has been to rehabilitate key facilities (for example highways in Latvia) and to restore services (for example public transportation in Russia and Kazakhstan) while encouraging cost recovery from beneficiaries and participation of the private sector in investment and management. The housing sector is also important in the transition countries because of its share in the stock of wealth, its role in the privatisation process and in the financial sector as a source of mortgageable assets.

Given the key role of local government in infrastructure, the Bank has been working directly with several Russian local authorities on improved budgeting and accounting systems, and in Bulgaria, Poland and Romania on decentralisation, local government reform and municipal finance. In several countries, the possibility of using the Bank's guarantee authority to encourage private sector participation in sectoral investments in transportation, energy (for example district heating) and water is being considered.

At the request of the G-7, the Bank has been working on developing energy strategies in certain transition countries with high-risk, Soviet-designed nuclear reactors. This effort has been carried out in close collaboration with the EBRD, the European Investment Bank, the International Energy Agency, the G-7, and the countries themselves. The Bank supports the necessary policy reforms and the financing of conventional power investments, while working to coordinate with other financing sources for nuclear power development and nuclear safety.

In the area of the environment, the Bank prepared in cooperation with the OECD an action programme for the overall European and Central Asian region. It identifies environmental priorities – selected on the basis of impact on health and cost effectiveness criteria – as well as investment policies and institutional prerequisites for successful implementation of the action plan.

The Bank also actively participates in developing prioritised action plans in the Baltic Sea, the Danube and Black Sea to restore their ecology and enhance cooperation among the littoral or riparian states. The last programme involves cooperation among seven states. Besides the Bank plays a key coordinating role among the five countries concerned with the preservation of the Aral Sea. On the basis of environmental strategy papers prepared for each CEE countries, the Bank has prepared a number of environmental projects.

10.4.5 Technical assistance and aid coordination

While the exact magnitude of financial assistance to Russia and the other former Soviet republics in the coming years remains somewhat uncertain, perhaps more immediate gains can be achieved through better targeted technical assistance and through appropriate aid coordination mechanisms. This is again an area where the Bank has a major responsibility.

As already suggested above, the importance of institutional constraints cannot be over-emphasized. It must be recognised from the start that the need for technical assistance is enormous and extremely urgent. The World Bank has shown its willingness to fund critical technical assistance requirements. While technical assistance operations are costly to prepare and supervise their impact is long run and usually less exposed to macro-economic instability and to changes in political balances and personalities.

Technical assistance is not only a key factor in the reform process, it is also often a prerequisite for the preparation of investment operations. Technical assistance loans (or loan components) are very management intensive — both in preparation and supervision — and the Bank faces considerable borrowing reluctance in view of the availability of grant financing from other donors. Concerted efforts by donors are required to ensure coherent policy advice, to articulate technical assistance and investment financing, and to alleviate the impact of absorptive capacity constraints.

The centrepiece of aid coordination is the Consultative Group (CG) process. Further to the coordination meeting in October 1992 in Tokyo, the Bank received a mandate to put together a coordinated approach for assistance to the CIS countries. In addition, it is gradually taking over from the Group of 24 in countries such as Bulgaria, Romania and Albania. The ideal for a CG meeting is to attain a compact: the government presents a comprehensive strategy and obtains in the course of the CG traceable assistance commitments. Since stabilisation is still a problem for many countries to obtain specific commitments already in the first CG is often impossible. The pre-CG's formula recognises this and puts the emphasis on coordinating technical assistance as a basis for full-fledged CG's over time.

One of the tasks for the World Bank in these CG meetings is to improve its own interaction with the European Union which is the single largest donor of technical assistance and which legitimately insists on putting its flag on the various activities it finances. Since 1992 the relationship has improved and the interaction is reducing duplication and enhancing the relevance and the quality of the technical assistance provided.

Table 10.3 World Bank commitments to the CEE and FSU countries (in million dollars and fiscal years)

Countries	As of June 30 1989	1990	1991	1992	1993	1994	Total
Albania (a)				41	44	47	132
Armenia (a)					12	28	40
Azrbaijan							
Belarus						170	170
Bulgaria			17	250	178	148	593
Croatia						128	128
Federal Czech and Slovak Republic			450	246			696
Czech Republic						80	80
Estonia					30	50	50
FYR (a) Macedonia						80	80
Georgia							
Hungary	1,954	366	550	200	413	129	3,612
Kazahstan						274	274
Kyrgyzstan a)					60	78	138
Latvia					45	25	70
Lithuania					60	26	86
Moldova					26	60	86
Poland		781	1,440	390	902	146	3,657
Romania (b)			180	650	120	401	1,351
Russian Federarion					1,370	1,520	2,890
Slovak Republic						135	135
Slovenia						80	80
Socialist Federal Rep. of Yugoslavia	3,117	692	300				4,109
Tajikistan							
Turkmenistan							
Ukraine					27		27
Uzbekistan						21	21
Total	5,071	1,839	2,937	1,777	3,285	3,626	18,535

(a) Albania, Armenia and Kyrgyzstan are the only countries in the region that received IDA credits. In the case of FYR of Macedonia, half of $80 million was an IDA credit. For all other countries the amounts represent IBRD loans.

(b) Romania borrowed more than $2 billion from IBRD in the 1970s but decided to reimburse everything in the 1980s.

Source: World Bank Annual Reports.

Table 10.4 IBRD loans and IDA credits outstanding as of June 30, 1994 (in million dollars)

Countries	IBRD Loans	IDA Credits
Albania		51
Armenia	1	3
Belarus	39	
Bosnia - Herzegovina and Federal Republic of Yugoslavia	1,652	
Bulgaria	248	
Croatia	99	
Czech Republic	341	
Estonia	28	
Hungary	2,174	
Kazahstan	122	41
Kyrgyzstan		
Latvia	36	
Lithuania	48	
Macedonia (FYR)	102	42
Moldova	79	
Poland	1,291	
Romania	543	
Russia	616	
Slovak Republic	178	
Slovenia	149	
Ukraine	1	
Uzbekistan	1	
Total	7,748	137

Source: World Bank 1994 Annual report.

10.4.6 Overall assessment of the World Bank's contribution

Two main questions can be raised in assessing the World Bank's performance in the Central and Eastern European economies in transition:

- Were the resources provided by the World Bank sufficient to support the transition process and sufficiently distributed among the countries concerned?
- Were the assistance strategies well designed for the specific conditions of the countries concerned?

a. Volume and allocation of resources

A closer look at Tables 10.3 and 10.4 suggests that the resources provided by the World Bank to the countries in transition were not as significant as might have been expected and were heavily concentrated in only a few countries:

- Total commitments to the region increased from $1.8 billion in fiscal year (FY) 90 to $3.6 billion in FY 94. This remains below the commitment volume of about $4.5 billion envisaged in the Bank's FY 94 budget.
- In terms of disbursements, the performance is even less impressive. Net disbursements over the last four fiscal years represent only $3.2 billion. Total outstanding IBRD loans and IDA credits to the region stood at $7.9 billion as of June 30, 1994 but about half of this amount represents loans made to Hungary and the former Socialist Federal Republic of Yugoslavia before the transition process really started.
- Indeed, commitments are heavily concentrated in a few countries: Hungary, Poland, Romania and since FY 93 Russia. Disbursements to Russia have only reached $600 million and have not yet started for Ukraine. Disbursements to countries such as Bulgaria and Belarus remain modest compared to their balance of payments needs.

Three points can be made, however, in defence of the Bank's performance:

- The Bank can only lend when appropriate economic policies are in place or for investment projects with a demonstrated economic viability. Such policies and projects take time to develop, however. Otherwise countries will only be accumulating debts while the Bank itself will have extended bad loans. Only a few of the region's countries (for example Albania, Armenia, Kyrgyzstan and the former Yugoslav Republic of Macedonia) have a level of per capita income that is low enough to make them eligible for concessionary IDA credits.
- Furthermore, the Bank's advisory and catalytic role is as least as important as its lending role. The Bank played a major role in preparing country economic memoranda, sector reports, in advising on institution building and in organising consultative group meetings and other aid coordination activities. The pioneering role of the

World Bank and of the International Finance Corporation paved the way for large scale privatisation in Russia and the subsequent flow of foreign direct investment.

• Procurement and disbursement under Bank loans have to follow very strict procedures with which new Bank members were initially not familiar. This explains part of the delays. Although these procedures are sometimes cumbersome, they have been established to ensure the most efficient use of the Bank's resources and to prevent corruption. These objectives remain particularly worthwhile in the context of the CEE and FSU countries.

b. Adequacy of country assistance strategies

A number of observations can be made on this issue:

• The Bank has been quick in recognising that the most pressing requirement in the early stages of the transition, particularly for the FSU countries, was technical assistance. Yet the Bank was originally not geared to the technical assistance business.

• Nevertheless, the Bank managed relatively well to provide technical assistance, financing it initially from its own budget and subsequently out of institution building loans. Cooperation with the PHARE and TACIS programmes of the European Community has improved over the years and the Bank's coordinating role is now well accepted.

• Through its 'rehabilitation loans' or its 'critical imports loans', the Bank provided balance of payments assistance with a relatively low conditionality in the initial stages of the transition. This was the right move, in some way the Bank's equivalent to the Fund's STF which was established only one year later. Yet the Bank deferred in this area to the Fund and did not sign any of these loans before the countries concerned had an IMF stabilisation programme.

• The Bank's subsequent emphasis on enterprise governance, restructuring and privatisation as well as on financial sector reform appears again well-founded, even if the preparation and the implementation of enterprise and financial sector adjustment programmes are proving far from easy.

• The Bank has also been right in focusing its human resources in the areas of safety nets and labour market policies, where the countries in transition face a huge challenge. It is too soon to say if the political will and the necessary implementation capacity can be mustered to create these mechanisms in time to avert a social explosion.

• Last but not least, the Bank's sectoral work in energy, agriculture, infrastructure, housing and the environment is providing the analytical foundations for sound investment projects within agreed priorities and sectoral policies. Although in other parts of the world the Bank has been frequently exposed to the criticism of non-governmental organisations that the projects it financed were harmful for the environment or for some social groups no institution has devoted so many resources in mapping out a strategy to reverse the dramatic deterioration of the environment in the CEE and FSU countries.

• Although less easy to measure, the contribution of the International Finance Corporation to the transition process is quite significant as its operations provide concrete examples of private investments encouraging the development of a new entrepreneurial culture.

Another criticism that has been addressed to the Bank is that there has been too much 'statism' in its philosophy and that it has not been sufficiently aggressive in promoting market-oriented reforms (Mizsei, 1994). It has been argued, for example, that in supporting the creation of the Hungarian State Holding Company, the Bank has been running the risk of generating a lobby group interested in slowing down privatisation. This criticism is largely unfounded: the Bank's objective has been enterprise reform which meant either privatisation or improved governance of those state owned enterprises which could not to be privatised in the short tun. The Bank encouraged Hungary to move faster towards privatisation but recognised that if there were enterprises which the Hungarian authorities, for various reasons, could not or did not want to privatise, the priority was to ensure that these enterprises were at least properly supervised and their management made accountable for their performance and/or restructuring efforts.

10.5 CONCLUSIONS

Let us come back to the five most fundamental points in this chapter:

• Everyone, including the Bretton Woods institutions, underestimated the difficulty of the transition process and the magnitude of the transition recession. This recession was associated with the temporary absence of an effective coordinating mechanism in the period between breakdown of the central planning and the establishment of market mechanisms. The depth of this recession was dangerous and could still jeopardise the socio-political sustainability of the transition process in some countries. Hence, the usefulness of the Bank's 'rehabilitation loans' or 'critical imports loans' and of the Fund's STF. The debate remains open whether the Bretton Woods institutions could have moved more quickly and more massively to soften the pains of transition.

- The most important component for a successful transition strategy is the establishment of the legal, institutional and human basis of a market economy. Massive and well coordinated technical assistance is needed, particularly for institution building. Although this is not by nature their primary mandate, the World Bank and the IMF have gone as far as they could in this direction.
- The painful task of stabilising the economy cannot be avoided. In fact the cost of not stabilising the economy is even greater. Yet, experience has demonstrated the crucial role of incomes policies, fiscal reform and the creation of social safety nets. The IMF and the World Bank have been right in emphasising these aspects both in their stabilisation programmes and in their policy-based lending.
- The hard core of the transition process consists in solving the combined problems of governance, restructuring and privatisation of major state-owned enterprises and the related problem of banking reform. The World Bank has been right in focusing its human and financial resources on this issue.
- The transition process cannot succeed without adequate external financial support, combined with open markets in the OECD countries. The Bretton Woods institutions form the cornerstone of that support. It would seem that overall they have been successful in the CEE and Baltic countries in catalysing international capital flows. It is too soon to assess definitely if their posture on Russia has been too lax or too restrictive. In any case Russia is rich in resources and might benefit from heavy capital reflows when its economy gets stabilised. Serious concern remains however on the adequacy of the present arrangement for the less privileged ex FSU countries, in particular Ukraine, Belarus as well as the poorer Central Asian and Caucasian Republics. It is for them that new G-10 or G-24 initiatives might be called for.

BIBLIOGRAPHY

BALCEROWICZ, L. (1993) *Common fallacies in the debate on the economic transition in Central and Eastern Europe*, EBRD Working Paper, no 11.

BOFINGER, P. and D. GROS (1992) 'A post-Soviet Payments Union: why and how' in J. Fleming and J.M.C. Rollo (eds), *Trade payments and adjustment in Central and Eastern Europe*, Royal Institute of International Affairs and EBRD.

BRUNO, M. (1992) 'Stabilisation and reform in Eastern Europe: preliminary evaluation', in *Eastern Europe in transition: from recession to growth*, World Bank Discussion Paper, no 196.

BUSINESS CENTRAL EUROPE (1993) 'IMF-Standing by', September.

CORICELLI, F. and A. REVENGA (1992) *Wage policy during the transition to a market economy: Poland 1990—91*, World Bank Discussion Paper, no 158.

DRABEK, Z. (1992) 'Convertibility or a payments union? - Convertibility' in J. Fleming and J.M.C. Rollo (eds), *Trade payments and Adjustment*, Royal Institute of International Affairs and EBRD.

GROS, D. (1993) *The Interstate bank: an end to monetary disintegration in the former Soviet Union?*, CEPS, Brussels.

GROS, D. (1994) *Monetary Aspects of the disintegration of the Soviet Union*, draft quoted by A. Steinherr.

IMF (1994a) *Financial relations among countries of the former Soviet Union*, IMF Economic Reviews.

IMF (1994b) *World Economic Outlook, May.*

KIEKENS, W. (1994) *Background report for the IMF Interim Committee*, April.

McKINNON, R. (1994) *Gradual versus rapid liberalisation in socialist economies*, International Centre for Economic Growth, San Francisco.

MIZSEI, K. (1994) 'The role of the Bretton Woods institutions in the transforming economies', in Brettton Woods Commission, *Bretton Woods: looking to the future*, July.

SACHS, J. (1994) 'Buying time for democracy', *European Brief*, April/May.

STEINHERR, A. (1994) *Does Eastern European reconstruction need more institutional support?*, Colloquium 'La négociation commerciale et financière internationale', Nice-Sophia Antipolis, June.

YERGIN, D. and T. GUSTAFSON (1994) *Russia 2010*, the CERA report, Nicholas Brealey Publishing, London.

11 Cross-Border Payment Systems and the European Monetary Union

Theo Peeters

11.1 INTRODUCTION

Payment systems have undergone profound transformation in recent years. The techniques of payment have been modified, with payment by cards and credit transfers taking a larger share of the total. In addition, with the integration of capital markets and the creation of the European Union (EU) internal market, more and larger payments are passing from one country to another and, hence, from one payment system to another.

The rapid increase in cross-border payments and, thus, in interfacing between payment systems has been assisted by technological innovations in telecommunications. Yet, the increase in the speed and volume of cross-border payments has not been accompanied by a comparable harmonisation or integration of payment systems and/or in the approach to risk management and supervision. This is, however, what one would expect to see forthcoming as a complement to the creation of the European Single Market. An efficient cross-border payment system is the obvious counterpart to an efficient cross-border trade system.

The need for higher efficiency and transparency in European payment systems will be further enhanced by the creation of an Economic and Monetary Union (EMU). The creation of the European System of Central Banks (ESCB) will, indeed, entail profound changes in the rules of the game for banking supervision and the control of systemic risks, and central bank involvement in payment systems.

The issues related to payment system design, management and supervision are a relatively recent concern in the European Union.

The central banks of the EU began to work together in the field of payments systems only in January 1991. Although important ground has been covered major issues remain unsettled. The Commission of the EU, under pressure of the consumers lobby, addressed cross-border retail payment issues already 5 or 6 years ago. Besides consumer policy issues, the Commission also contributed in an important way to clarify legal issues and stimulated European banking standards and, more generally, to the modernisation of the systems for cross-border payments.

The Center for European Policy Studies (CEPS) recently published a report which reflects the discussions of a working party with specialists from various horizons in the private and public sector. This working party, which we had the privilege to chair, reviewed the issues while looking for consensus and possible solutions. The reader is referred to this report (Mortensen, 1994) for a more in depth discussion and an overview of the extensive and rapidly increasing literature on the subject. While drawing freely from this report, this chapter is not a resumé as such but rather a personal view on some highlights and key issues.

A useful starting point for this approach is the distinction between small-value (retail) and large-value (wholesale) payments. Small-value cross-border payments in Europe today are a major concern to consumers and consumer organisations. This concern is reflected in initiatives from the European Commission. Large-value cross-border payments are closely related with growing settlement risk and systemic risk. They have attracted major attention from central bank governors.

Voluminous reports have been written on both issues and proposals put forward. What are some of the key issues, and what do they mean for the future of European central banking will be the subject of the following three sections. But in order to set a general framework for the rest of this paper, we briefly remind the reader of the essence of a payment system i.e.:

'the set of arrangements for the discharge of the obligations assumed by economic agents whenever they acquire real or financial resources. In non-barter economies such obligations are discharged through the transfer of title of ownership of a narrow set of claims which, by the virtue of their wide acceptability, are known as 'money' (the 'settlement medium'). The payment system, therefore, is a set of mechanisms for the transfer of money among agents. Its

constituents comprise the institutions providing payment services, the various forms of money, the means of transferring them, including message instructions and communications channels, and the contractual relationships linking the parties concerned' (Borio and Van Den Bergh, 1993, p.8).

11.2 CROSS-BORDER SMALL-VALUE PAYMENTS

Small-value cross-border payments have come under close scrutiny by the European Commission at least since 1988. Proposals for improvement have been put forward in the four main payment categories: cash, credit transfers, cheques, and payment cards. Yet, credit transfers, being the most important form of cross-border payment in terms of value and the source of most problems, have received most of the attention.

Small-value transfer systems are defined as those systems that meet the payment needs of individuals and businesses for ordinary transactions in the economy. A feature that clearly distinguishes small-value transfer systems from large-value transfer systems is their large number. Small-value transfer systems should be extremely versatile: they must be able to handle payments for a large variety of transactions. They must also have a large processing capacity to support the enormous daily volume of transactions that take place in a market economy. Moreover, small-value transfer systems support virtually every participant in the economy. Accordingly, the market for small-value transfer services is very large. In a competitive environment with product differentiation we can, therefore, expect a variety of competing systems.

Although the average size of a payment processed through a small-value transfer system is typically quite small, some individual transactions are quite substantial in size, since these systems (have to) support also payments between corporations. In fact, small-value systems routinely handle individual transactions valued in the millions of dollars. However, the daily total value of all transactions processed through these systems, is quite small compared with the value processed through large-value payments systems (Pingitzer and Summers, 1994, p. 101-107). The customers of the small-value payment systems are far from a homogeneous group. Their interest in the service provided as well as their requirements therefore diverge considerably. This latter characteristic is not always adequately accounted for in criticisms of the costs and performance of small-value payment systems.

According to the European Commission essential improvements are required with respect to transparency, speed, and reliability, as well as of the cost of cross-border retail payments, especially of the credit transfers. The purpose of studies, commissioned by the EU about these aspects (Retail Banking Research Ltd, 1993 and 1994), was to evaluate the level of transparency of service conditions as well as the performance of remote cross-border payments in all member states of the EU and the extent to which guidelines agreed with the banking community are being applied. Remote payments are all those implying the process of sending a payment across a border by an originator remaining in his country of residence. In particular the Commission wished to establish: the availability of information about such transfers; how transparent conditions and prices are to customers; the prices charged to senders and recipients; the extent of double charging, and the time taken for such transfers to occur.

The studies involved two exercises set to run in parallel: a transfer exercise between accounts in the twelve EU member states, and a market research exercise focusing on the level of information provided by banks on cross-border transfers. In the former study, instructions were given to send an amount equivalent to 100 ECU with a request that all charges be paid by the sender. Furthermore, the instructions were given to ensure that the beneficiary should receive the net amount in his account -in his own currency.

According to the published report of the 1994 study, the cost of transfers for 1044 successful cross-border transfers amounted to an average of 25.4 ECU. Explicit sender charges amounted to 22.39 ECU, foreign exchange costs to 0.42 ECU and receiver charges to 2.59 ECU (see Table 11.1).

The highest (average) level of explicit sender charges was found in Portugal, France and the United Kingdom-member states where credit transfers account for a very low share of domestic payments. Low levels of sender charges were found in Luxembourg, Spain, the Netherlands and Italy, where credit transfers typically constitute a dominant feature of domestic payment systems. Therefore, cost-effective systems of routing this category of payments are already in place and can more easily be exploited for at least part of the routing of a cross-border credit transfer.

Table 11.1 Total transfer costs by type of cost and sender country (average cost in ECU, rankings in brackets*)

Country	Explicit sender charges		Receiver		Sender charges exchange		Total	
Belgium	21.62	(7)	0.67	(2)	0.78	(10)	23.06	(6)
Denmark	20.11	(5)	0.69	(3)	0.39	(8)	21.19	(14)
France	30.33	(11)	2.56	(9)	0.12	(2)	33.01	(12)
Germany	25.20	(9)	0.75	(4)	0.21	(6)	26.16	(7)
Greece	20.41	(6)	8.37	(12)	4.01	(12)	32.78	(10)
Ireland	22.42	(8)	4.59	(11)	0.12	(2)	27.13	(9)
Italy	18.91	(4)	1.87	(6)	0.10	(1)	20.88	(3)
Luxembourg	13.05	(1)	2.02	(8)	0.67	(9)	15.75	(1)
Netherlands	17.53	(3)	1.01	(6)	0.30	(7)	18.84	(2)
Portugal	26.18	(10)	0.43	(1)	0.13	(4)	26.75	(8)
Spain	15.20	(2)	6.69	(10)	0.15	(5)	22.04	(5)
United Kingdom	30.57	(12)	1.27	(7)	1.14	(11)	32.99	(11)
EU Average	22.39		2.59		0.42		25.41	

* 1 is cheapest, 12 most expensive
Source: Retail Banking Research Ltd, (1994).

The transfers were ordered with the request that all charges should be paid by the payer. Nevertheless, receiver charges, incurred by the beneficiary, were applied in 36% of the cases studied. As seen from the perspective of the sender country they ranged from a low of 0.41 ECU for transfers initiated in Portugal to more than 8 ECU for transfers initiated in Greece. Why receiver charges should show such large variations between sender countries is somewhat obscure, but is not analyzed in the survey. However, when analyzed from the point of view of the receiver country, the highest levels were found, again, in the countries where sender charges are high: France, Portugal and the United Kingdom. Greece has the highest receiver charges, averaging 21 Ecu for all transfers with a deduction, but the proportion of transfers received that incurred a deduction was rather small.

The second part of the survey included a review of quoted sender charges for transfers of 100 ECU and 2,500 ECU. The principal finding (see Table 11.2) was that the average quoted sender charges for 2,500 ECU (20.2 ECU on average for the EC) was only 25 % higher than the charge for sending 100 ECU (16.9 ECU). Furthermore, the average quoted sender charge was 5.5 ECU lower than the effective, explicit sender charge measured in the first part of the survey.

Table 11.2 Average quoted sender charges (in ECU) for an urgent transfer, by country (for 100 and 2,500 ECU transfers)

Country	Average charge for sending 100 ECU	Average charge for sending 2,500 ECU
Belgium	12.0	15.2
Denmark	17.7	18.4
France	25.5	26.1
Germany	17.4	19.7
Greece	19.1	17.6
Ireland	19.8	20.3
Italy	13.4	16.5
Luxembourg	9.5	12.3
Netherlands	11.4	12.7
Portugal	20.3	39.2
Spain	21.2	13.9
UK	22.2	23.4
EU Average	16.9	20.2

Fee as % of amount sent 16.9% 0.81%
Source: Retail Banking Research Ltd., (1994).

Several comments are in order here. First, payment systems are to a large extent a fixed cost business. This makes retail payments, of course, relatively expensive. This is especially true for cross-border transfers which have to rely on routing through at least two domestic payment systems. Until ways are found to overcome the extra costs that result from the diversity between the national payment systems, the cost of cross-border small-value transfers will continue to be out of line with similar domestic transactions.

The volume of cross-border retail payments remains small. The consequent lack of economies of scale does not justify large investments in this market segment. Banks have focused their efforts mainly on improving the domestic payment systems. In 1991 cross-border retail payments for all EU-member states amounted to only 1.3% of all payments transactions. In value terms the importance was even smaller i.e.: 0.1% of the total value of payments transactions.

Ways to cut costs may come from the second European banking directive that, through the transparency and reciprocity principles, guarantees banks direct access to foreign clearing systems. However, standardization of techniques and procedures across borders is a prerequisite for large scale automatization and cost reductions. No uniform solution is yet in sight throughout the EU. Improvements of correspondent banking networks are therefore likely to continue to co-exist alongside the linkage of automated domestic clearing systems.

A second factor which distorts cost comparisons between domestic and cross-border transfers are that domestic payment systems in general benefit from more or less heavy cross-subsidizations whereas cross-border payments are operated more on the basis of full-cost charging. To the extent that consumer organisations and officials insist that these difference should disappear, the solution will come more from less cross-subsidization and, therefore, higher domestic charges, rather than from more cross-subsidization and lower charges for cross-border transactions.

Thirdly, cross-border payments do not only entail transfer charges. They also result in currency conversion costs. These latter costs will only disappear when a single currency is established in stage three of the EMU-programme.

It is against this background that the EU-Commission in a draft directive on Transparency and Performance of Remote Cross-Border Payments, insists on three criteria for improvement i.e.:

- the institution shall supply its customers with clearly *written information* about the services it provides to effect or receive remote cross-border payments;
- *double charging* should be eliminated. 'An institution shall be obliged to execute the credit transfer for the full amount thereof unless the originator authorized the making of a deduction therefrom. The only charges which may be deducted by the institution of the beneficiary are those relating to the administration of his account, where applicable, and if so they shall not be determined by the cross-border character of the payment';
- an institution should execute a credit transfer *in good time*. In the absence of agreement to the contrary the institution shall be obliged to execute the credit transfer at the latest by the end of the business

day following receipt of the payment order. The institution of the originator shall be responsible to the originator for ensuring that the credit transfer is completed no later than the end of the sixth business day following receipt of the payment order from the originator.

How and when these obligations will be made effective remains an open question.

Elimination of double charging is a fine principle. But it implies cost and revenue sharing agreements among a complex and highly diversified network of banks throughout Europe. In Europe we have 15,000 credit institutions. Not everyone of them can conclude direct bilateral arrangements with all the other 14,999 banks. Cross-border transfers will, therefore, most of the time require a multilateral rather than a bilateral operation. It is very difficult to know in advance the number of banks that will (have to) intervene in a particular cross-border transfer. Setting the charges and commissions beforehand will often be impossible for the originator bank. Some possibilities for improvements in the short and in the long run have been suggested in a recent study for the European Commission (Belgische Vereniging der Banken, 1994). The key-answer is again further standardization and the generalization of the SWIFT-standards for cross-border payments. In combination with interbank agreements for the compensation of the receiver banks, procedures for the retrocession of interbank commissions, the storage by computer of the commissions due, and periodic settlement in favour of the beneficiary banks, these technical improvements can provide a solution. These agreements should be negotiated in consultation with the services in charge of competition policy of the EU-Commission.

A limited number of multilateral interbank agreements could go a long way towards more efficient mechanisms for cross-border small-value payments. The number of fee schedules each foreign correspondent bank should be familiar with would, indeed, be drastically cut. Such an approach would also leave room for competing systems. And it would bypass, for the time being, the technical nightmare of the link at the Community level of the existing domestic clearing systems, which has been suggested by the European Commission. However, the European banks will have to work together towards greater standardization and centralization of the cross-border payments process if they want to avoid being overtaken by the competition, in particular by the card-companies.

The objective of making cross-border transfers as quick and efficient as are transfers within one and the same member state, remains a crucial objective of the single European market programme. But the cost structure of cross-border credit transfers will remain for quite some time significantly different from that of domestic payments and, therefore, more expensive. Cross-border credit transfers will indeed entail costs and administrative complications, even after the introduction of a single currency, that are absent in domestic payment systems. Efforts are being made to obtain a reduction of these costs, to simplify administrative complications, and to enhance the transparency of the conditions. But the success of these efforts will also depend on the modernization of the domestic payment systems in the EU member states. EU legislation alone is not enough.

In the meantime, the intelligent consumer prefers the most cost-efficient cross-border small-value payment system available today, which is the service offered by the card companies. But although the importance of this service continues to grow, it has immediately been objected, rightly so, that this service is not really a payment system in the sense that it is accessible to everybody and for all possible transactions at every moment.

11.3 CROSS-BORDER LARGE-VALUE PAYMENTS

In recent years, technological and financial innovation and the development of financial markets have spurred an exponential growth in large payment operations. The stability of the financial system has come to depend more and more on the proper functioning of interbank clearing and settlement arrangements. Indeed, large-value transfer systems supporting the interbank markets have a direct bearing not only on the safe and efficient operation of domestic money and capital markets. Large-value transfer systems increasingly play an international role. Their safe and efficient operation has become a major concern for policymakers and banking practitioners.

Participants in markets such as, interbank, securities, foreign exchange, and business-to-business or wholesale naturally seek bank payment services and payment mechanisms that can meet their needs for reliability, security, accuracy, and timeliness. To meet these needs, specialised large-value transfer systems have evolved. With the integration of financial markets, national interbank payment systems have become more interdependent. Accordingly, the concept of a global payment system, consisting of a network of payment relations encompassing many countries, has come to the fore.

Central banks are following these developments with great attention and growing concern. Not only are they directly involved as operators in the systems. Their regulatory and prudential control responsibilities make them especially alert to the liquidity and credit risks inherent in large-value payment systems since these risks could adversely affect public confidence. The potential disruption of large-value payments by its nature, would have far-reaching repercussions not only on the monetary system but also on the economy as a whole.

The wide range of existing systems can be characterized in terms of two basic models (Angelini, 1994) i.e.: net versus gross settlement systems. In *net settlement systems* (also called clearing or netting systems) transactions are netted against each other during the business day. This can be done either bilaterally or multilaterally through a central agent; in either case payments normally become irrevocable, or final, only at the end of the day, when balances are settled. Settlement in commercial bank money is still predominant in intra-European cross-border payments, as well as in international payments in general. Clearing with end-of-day settlement in central bank money has become the dominant mode in European domestic payment systems.

The advantages and pitfalls of clearing systems are well-known (Padoa-Schioppa, 1994). The main advantage, of course, is the substantial reduction in the holding of non-interest bearing central bank money. This is made possible since the latter is only used to assure final payment in good money of the end-of-day net obligations. The main pitfall has traditionally been the indirect risk deriving from the multilateral nature of the netting. Since intraday payments are provisional, i.e. they do not become good funds until settlement time, and since banks most of the time during the day do not send an equal amount of payments than they receive, debit and credit balances will accumulate. The intraday debit or credit balances, or daylight overdrafts, give rise to liquidity as well as credit risks because one or more banks incurring daylight overdrafts may not be able to fund their positions by the time they come due.

These daylight overdrafts have been increasingly criticized on different grounds. One main criticism is that the total amount of gross transactions to be settled has grown substantially in relation not only to central bank money but also to large multiples of commercial banks' capital. Risk considerations, therefore, become of growing practical relevance. Further, these traditional risks have become 'systemic' in that the default of a bank with a large debit position may in turn cause direct creditors to become insolvent. The failure of one participant could trigger a chain reaction leading to the collapse of the entire system. Finally, a moral hazard problem arises since most clearing systems rely on the supply of end-of-day settlement services by a central bank. If a bank suddenly defaults, its counterparts may expect central banks to prevent a crisis from erupting. Systemic risk is perceived to have outgrown individual risk. Netting schemes, in the view of central banks, have, therefore, gradually moved to a situation in which participants reap most of the benefits and the pitfalls are left to the central bank.

Perception of these problems has raised serious concerns among central banks. As lender of last resort the central banks can always prevent a crisis from erupting. But if they always do and if market participants would start to act on this assumption, the very essence of commercial banking as a private risk-taking business would be lost. A central bank indeed needs to provide enough liquidity in the financial system to ensure its smooth functioning. But at the same time central bank money should be sufficiently rare in order to encourage its efficient use and to keep adequate control over the money supply.

Risk reduction programmes and substantial changes in interbank mechanisms are being implemented with the aim to protect the stability of financial markets which are critically dependent on the reliability and efficiency of interbank payment networks. In the general model of a deferred net settlement system, settlement does not occur payment-by-payment, but at designated times during the day. Between designated settlement times payments exchanged are multilaterally netted, resulting in one net obligation for each net debtor bank which falls due at settlement time. Netting systems thus allow a significant reduction in intraday liquidity needed to settle large payments. And these liquidity needs are met by the *de facto* extension of credit among the participants in the system. Central banks should, therefore, feel sufficiently confident about the appropriateness of the risk management controls of the netting schemes.

Minimum standards -the so-called six Lamfalussy-standards published by the Bank for International Settlements (see Appendix I)- have come into use for judging the adequacy and the design of cross-border multi-currency netting systems. Risk management measures of netting schemes cover a wide range: the restriction on direct access to supervised credit institutions, control on bilateral and multilateral credit exposures, collateralisation of debit exposures, procedures for the resolution of settlement failures, including changes in the legal framework to ensure the enforceability of bilateral and multilateral netting.

An alternative response to the often complex risk management measures of netting schemes is found in the development and expansion of *real-time gross settlement systems* (RTGS). In RTGS payment messages are credited or debited to accounts that participating institutions hold with the central bank. The adjective 'gross' means that payments are settled individually, without a preliminary netting phase. Three main RTGS-types can be distinguished: RTGS (i) with and (ii) without daylight overdrafts, and (iii) queuing systems.

RTGS *with* daylight overdraft will allow participants to overdraw their account with the central bank during the business day. Thus, a sending bank may effect a real time transfer of funds even when its centralized account is empty. Payments become 'final' in real time, since central bank money is transferred to the receiving bank's account regardless of the actual availability of reserves on the sender's account.

In RTGS *without* overdrafts a payment is rejected if the sender bank's centralized account does not have sufficient funds to cover it. A larger volume of reserves is, therefore, required to settle on a gross basis without adequate overdrafts. The provision of adequate liquidity in the system is, thus, a key issue under RTGS.

A queuing system can be viewed as an intermediate configuration between a net settlement system and a gross system without daylight overdrafts. No central bank credit is available but payment messages lacking coverage are not automatically rejected. They are entered into a waiting queue and processed on a FIFO (first in, first out) basis as soon as enough reserves flow in. But a queuing system is vulnerable to gridlock if the queue leads to congestion and, therefore, to a breakdown of the payment flows.

The advantages, cost, and the risks of net versus gross settlement systems are still the subject of further research and of heated debate between private market operators and official regulators and central banks.

In a nutshell, real-time gross settlement for large-value payments favoured by central bankers and supervisors over net settlement systems reduce settlement risk and systemic risk, provided gridlock can be avoided. This in turn depends on the availability of back-up liquidity to keep the system running smoothly. The advantages of RTGS in terms of risk control, integrity, security, and stability have, therefore, to be considered against the extra costs they entail. It is not obvious that the potential gains from risk reduction as seen by the supervisors, are always weighted adequately against the additional costs incurred by the private banking sector.

In the meantime significant steps are being taken to improve risk management in a number of respects. One is better identification and transparency of credit and liquidity exposures, notably through real-time monitoring of the positions of participants. A second step is a better distribution of those exposures, for example through delivery-against-payment mechanisms in securities markets, which achieve the simultaneous settlement of the two legs of the trades. A third measure is better control, for example through wider use of bilateral and multilateral limits on participants' positions and of collateral requirements. A fourth condition consists of greater certainty of settlement for sub-sets of transactions, as can be gained through a shortening of settlement lags, notably through the introduction of RTGS.

But an important challenge remains, namely the introduction of appropriate liquidity-pooling and loss-sharing mechanisms to ensure settlement in specific systems in the event of a failure to settle on the part of individual participants. In the absence of adequate safeguards in this respect, the resolution of a settlement failure relies on the ability of the central bank to provide liquidity assistance which may be to the detriment of transparency and incentives for prudent behaviour.

In traditional large-value payment systems gross settlement in central bank money was prohibitively expensive. Participants indeed needed to hold very high levels of non-interest bearing reserves to settle all their gross obligations in central bank money and in the course of the business day. Although much lower today, these costs are still relevant. It is no accident that RTGS is found chiefly in countries where the central bank supplies cost-free daylight overdrafts. Progress in payment technology and the increase in velocity will not be sufficient to finance the larger volume of reserves required to settle on a gross basis. Queuing, compulsory reserves, overdrafts, limits, pricing and collateral in overdrafts are all elements of the architecture of RTGS-systems. But the trade-off between efficiency and stability and the operational complexities leave ample room for choice and argument between net and gross settlement systems. The higher cost associated with RTGS is generally accepted. It is, therefore, reasonable that central banks should bear part of these higher costs as a counterpart for the reduction in systemic risk which they can expect.

Can we assume that with a complete transition to RTGS systemic risk would disappear? One might be tempted to answer positively because, almost by definition, a sequence of final payments cannot be unwound. In reality this might turn out differently because it may be difficult to separate settlement risk from the risk of a domino-effect in payment-credit relationships. Failure of one bank to meet a payment obligation at the time due may still set in motion a chain reaction once the density of interbank payment flows becomes very high. Even under RTGS risk reduction rather than risk elimination remains the name of the game (Padoa-Schioppa, 1994, p. 26). Compared with clearing systems the overall risk is reduced. Making payments in central bank money on a gross basis allows operators to buy lower risk levels at the (opportunity) cost of holding larger reserves on interest-free central bank accounts. But market operators today continue to argue that the risk reduction that RTGS provides is not always an adequate compensation for the higher costs those systems entail. Whereas in netting schemes central banks claim that participants reap most of the benefits and leave the pitfalls to the central banks, market operators maintain that RTGS tilts the cost-benefit balance against them in favour of the central banks.

RTGS and netting systems will, therefore, continue to co-exist for quite some time. This is the view of the Committee of EU Central Bank Governors (1993) in their report on 'Minimum common features for domestic payment systems'. It is indeed reasonable to expect that, for certain classes of payments, netting systems will continue to be the cheapest mode. There are payments for which the time value of money for intraday lags are not relevant. For a summary of these minimum common features see Appendix II. But the co-existence of netting schemes, even if they comply with the minimum standards, will remain a source of systemic risk by itself.

The interests of the various constituencies i.e. consumers, business, financial institutions, monetary authorities - differ a lot. And the solutions offered in the various countries are not the same. Diversity rather than convergence is still a major characteristic when one compares European domestic payment systems. To reap the full benefits of the single market for financial services greater homogeneity will, however, be required. Can we expect automatic convergence to be brought about only on the basis of competition among market operators? Or is discretionary, regulatory action needed as claimed by monetary authorities?

The answer to these questions depends critically on the time horizon of the various actors and their assumption about future developments. It is sensible in this respect to distinguish between the current monetary-financial regime and an expected regime change in the future that will result from a single currency under the European monetary union. The implications for intra-European payment systems are much more drastic in case of a change in the regime. Market competition alone will then not be sufficient to bring about (cost) efficient as well as stable and secure intra-European payment systems. Given the long lead time needed to prepare and implement major innovations in payment systems, it is normal for European central banks to worry about measures that, not only can strengthen the existing systems but also to prepare for a regime change that is anticipated before the end of this decade.

11.4 CROSS-BORDER PAYMENTS AND THE FUTURE ROLE OF THE EUROPEAN CENTRAL BANK

Central banks are directly concerned with the smooth functioning of the payment system. A safe and efficient payment system is critical to the maintenance of sound banking and financial markets and to the execution of monetary policy. Overseeing the functioning of the payment system is an important mission of the central bank together with the control over the supply of central bank money and the supervision of commercial banks. Monetary policy, payment systems, and banking supervision are three complementary and deeply interlinked aspects of central banking. The interactions between these three missions are such that they are often difficult to disentangle.

A direct linkage exists between the payment system and the

execution of monetary policy because of the influence of payment system operations on the public's use of the money stock. The float that normally results from payment processing inefficiencies and time-lags can affect monetary policy, just as malfunctions do in the clearing and settlement process. A central bank interacts with the payment system in order to inject (or drain) reserves into (from) the banking system. However, the level of reserves that is needed to assure the smooth functioning of payment settlements is not always necessarily the same as that needed for monetary control purposes. RTGS with no overdrafts for example will require more frequent injections of reserves by the central bank to avoid the built-up of excessive intraday cash shortfalls that would cause settlement delays. An important two way interaction also exists between the payment process and the stability of the banking and financial systems. Disruptions in the payment system have the potential to weaken confidence in individual financial institutions. Conversely, problems in bank supervision have the potential to trigger disruptions in the payment system.

A complex, delicate balance characterizes the central bank's multiple responsibilities in the payments area. Against the background of the internationalization of economies and markets, it are the multiplicity of currencies, the lack of a single legal system, and the difficulty of creating international institutions that increase the burden for cooperative, voluntary arrangements between national central banks. These issues become even more difficult to handle if we look at the prospects and the requirements for intra-European cross-border payments in connection with the Maastricht Treaty and EMU.

Financial structure and practices within the major EU countries have been changing at different speeds, and some structural differences have remained and in some cases have become even more pronounced. The United Kingdom has seen the fastest growth of liquidity-intensive markets and practices, while the development of liquid money markets is lagging in Germany. The role of the various central banks differs accordingly. The Bank of England is more focused on an active management of liquidity combined with careful regulation and supervision of the financial sector, whereas the German Bundesbank has generally taken a less interventionist approach to financial markets, preferring instead to concentrate its efforts on achieving its monetary policy objectives. With the completion of the single European financial market, competition in financial services is likely to spread liquidity-intensive markets and practices across Europe, including the DM-markets.

The European System of Central Banks (ESCB) will be superimposed onto these dynamically evolving financial structures and practices. But the institutional set-up envisaged for stage 3 of EMU is based on a centralized implementation of monetary policy with the maintenance of price stability as the explicit primary objective. Supervision of banking institutions, on the contrary, is decentralized at the national level. The maintenance of stable financial and payment systems rests in the first place with the national monetary authorities. However, it will be necessary to determine whether a decentralized payment system is the most efficient and safe solution, whether it is compatible with the exercise of other central bank functions, and whether it is consistent with the needs and characteristics of the European financial market.

In particular, lender-of-last-resort operations can no longer be undertaken by national central banks in stage 3 of EMU. Such operations may have monetary effects and may be costly in terms of central bank resources. It is, therefore, difficult to envisage a departure from a centrally managed supply of central bank money. This will seriously constrain central banks with providing liquidity support to national payment systems. This may increase the risk of gridlock and systemic failures in the event of a financial market crash.

Finally, a delicate balance derives from the safety net aspects of the central bank involvement in the payment system. Relevant components of the safety net in this regard can e.g. include, the central bank's ability to manage access to the payment system and to provide emergency liquidity assistance to participants. These components must be judiciously managed to ensure that they are not abused. But under circumstances when they are most needed, i.e. in crisis situations, action may have to be taken almost immediately leaving not much room and time for consultation and coordination between national and Community authorities. The safety net of the lender-of-last-resort can provide a useful tool for ensuring that the financial institutions do not fail prematurely and that the integrity of the financial system is maintained. But it should be activated only in close combination with the supervisory and regulatory oversight of the banking system. It is not clear today whether the institutional set-up for stage 3 of EMU will meets this requirement.

11.5 CONCLUSION

The last two decades have been a period of momentous change for the financial services industry in Europe and worldwide. As an integral part of that industry, payment services have not been left unaffected. Rapid technological innovation, deregulation, greater volatility of asset prices, and integration of financial markets in Europe and worldwide have gone hand in hand with a surge in the volume and value of payments both within and, above all, across national borders. They have resulted in profound changes in payment arrangements and the process is still well underway.

The rapid increase in cross-border payments and, thus, in interfacing between payment systems has been assisted by technological innovations in the field of telecommunication. But the increase in the speed and volume of cross-border payments has not been accompanied by a comparable harmonization or approximation of the jurisdiction of payment systems and/or in the approach to risk management and supervision. As for the structure and development of European payment systems they show a complex diversity that may conflict with a deepening of the single market for financial services. The need for higher efficiency and transparency in European payment systems will be further enhanced by the moves toward Economic and Monetary Union.

In order to ensure the appropriate functioning of the single European market, significant improvements of intra-European cross-border transfers of small-value, retail payments are required. The objective is to make these transfers as quickly and efficiently as those within one and the same member state. This requires a high degree of transparency with respect to prices and payment delays, and the elimination of double charging. But as long as cross-border retail payments must be carried out wholly or partially outside the national clearing systems, they will entail a level of costs significantly in excess of comparable transactions within national payment systems. Furthermore, cross-border transactions rarely benefit from the cross-subsidization and cost-sharing features that are common practice in domestic payments. It is, therefore, expected that the charges for cross-border retail payments - excluding the currency conversion costs - will continue for quite some time to exceed those for domestic retail payments. Cost-cutting for cross-border retail payments will continue thanks to the standardization of techniques and procedures that will allow large scale automatization. However, for the time being the volumes remain too small.

EU central banks have agreed that each member state should have an RTGS into which as many large-value payments as possible should be channelled. In accordance with the principle of decentralisation the new payment arrangement for stage 3 will be composed of one RTGS in each country participating in the monetary union and the interlinking of these domestic facilities to process cross-border payments within the system. However, the creation of this new system will not rule out the continued existence of correspondent banking arrangements and net settlement systems, including their cross-border enlargement and efficiency improvements, particularly for small-value payments.

There is growing concern, particularly among central bankers and banking supervisors, that the pronounced increase in large-value cross-border payments in recent years has resulted in a rise in systemic risks, notwithstanding the fact that examples of gridlock and/or systemic failures are rare. Risk control and risk reduction are the overriding preoccupations in large-value payment systems, especially for cross-border transactions. These risks can be dealt with either through enhancement of the safety features of net settlement systems or a more widespread rise of gross settlement systems. In general the official attitude favours a universal move towards real time gross settlement. Market operators, however, are reluctant to shoulder the higher costs of RTGS. They question whether the extra insurance premium that they have to pay because of the higher costs of RTGS is worth the extra safety which those systems offer. For the supervisory authorities the answer is apparently an unqualified yes. Technological innovation together with the rising costs to participants in netting schemes of the risk reduction measures introduced to improve such systems, explain why the development and expansion of RTGS has become a central element in the reform of European interbank payment systems. At the same time it is accepted that RTGS and netting systems should and will co-exist.

The provision of adequate liquidity is of critical importance for the smooth functioning of RTGS. The availability of central bank money at any time of the day in RTGS can lower risks and improve efficiency. But the terms upon which central bank money should be provided (price, the amount of overdrafts, and especially collateral) will need to be agreed upon firmly. The risk reduction and efficiency improvements generated by greater central bank presence in large-value payment systems must not be offset by a weakening of market-selfdiscipline. While central banks should accept that they must bear part of the higher costs associated with the further spread of RTGS, they should not depart from the classic principles regarding lending-of-last-resort. It means that some element of discretionality should be preserved by central banks for the provision of intraday central bank money. Second, the cost to commercial banks of this advance of liquidity should not be negligible. And, finally, intraday credit by the central bank should always be covered by adequate collateral.

It was also argued in this chapter that even with a complete transition to RTGS, systemic risk would not completely disappear. Failure of one bank to meet a payment obligation may still set in motion a chain reaction. Even RTGS cannot guarantee risk elimination, but only risk reduction.

To conclude, a look at the issue of the development of intra-European cross-border payments and the future role of the European central bank, reveals the importance to recognize the complementarity and close links between the various aspects of central banking. But the EU single market rules - notably the rule of home country control over credit institutions - puts the supervision of banks and of the operation of payment systems largely in the hands of national authorities. However, in stage III of EMU, monetary policy will be concentrated in the European central bank. It is not obvious whether the solution of a decentralized supervision over the payment system combined with a centralization of monetary policy - and therefore of the function to provide liquidity to the payment system - is the most efficient and safe solution. The level of reserves needed to ensure sufficient liquidity in a gross settlement system is not necessarily the same at all times as what is needed for monetary control purposes. It is not evident that the potential conflict of interest that may arise in this respect -particularly in crisis situations- can be resolved through the rather vague provision in the Maastricht Treaty which charges the European System of Central Banks, as one of its four main tasks, to 'promote the efficiency of cross-border payments'. The authorities, however, feel confident that from a practical point of view they will be able to keep things under control.

APPENDIX 11.1

Minimum Standards for the Design and Operation of Cross-Border and Multi-Currency Netting and Settlement Schemes (Recommendations of the Committee on Interbank Netting Schemes, BIS, November 1990)

I. Netting schemes should have a well founded legal basis under all relevant jurisdictions.

II. Netting scheme participants should have a clear understanding of the impact of the particular scheme on each of the financial risks affected by the netting process.

III. Multilateral netting systems should have clearly defined procedures for the management of credit risks and liquidity risks which specify the respective responsibilities of the netting scheme and the participants. These procedures should also ensure that all parties have both the incentive and the capabilities to manage and contain each of the risks they bear and that limits are placed on the maximum level of credit exposure that can be produced by each participant.

IV. Multilateral netting systems should, at a minimum be capable of ensuring the timely completion of daily settlements in the event of an inability to settle by the participant with the largest single net-debit position.

V. Multilateral netting systems should have objective and publicly disclosed criteria for admission which permit fair and open access.

VI. All netting schemes should ensure the operational reliability of technical systems and the availability of back-up facilities capable of completing daily processing requirements.

APPENDIX 11.2

Summarized list of Principles from the Report on 'Minimum Common Features for Domestic Payment Systems'
by the Working Group on Payment Systems of EU Central Bank Governors, Nov. 1993

Principle 1 : As a rule, only central banks and credit institutions, as defined under the Second Banking Coordination Directive, can be admitted as direct participants in funds transfer systems which process third-party payments.

Principle 2 : No discrimination can be made between home-based credit institutions and credit institutions licensed in other EU countries which ask to participate in local interbank funds transfer systems, either through their local branches or directly from another Member State (remote access).
Principle 3 : Access criteria to interbank funds transfer systems should be laid down in a public document.
Principle 4 : As soon as feasible, every member state should have a real-time gross-settlement system into which as many large-value payments as possible should be channelled.
Principle 5 : Provided they settle at the central bank, large-value net-settlement systems may continue to operate in parallel with real-time gross-settlement system.
Principle 6 : As a part of their oversight function, EU central banks will assess the scale and the nature of the settlement risks in all interbank funds transfer systems operating in their country.
Principle 7 : The legal basis of domestic payments should be sound and enforceable.
Principle 8 : Compatible banking standards and efficiency channels of communication between EU payments are desirable.
Principle 9 : The pricing policies of EU central banks, in respect of payments systems functions, will aim at the avoidance of any competitive distortion within the context of the Single Market and in preparation for EMU.
Principle 10 : The overlap between operating hours of the major EU interbank funds transfer systems (and in particular the hours of RTGS systems) is necessary and could be increased in order to facilitate cross-border payments and delivery-versus-payment mechanisms.

BIBLIOGRAPHY

ANGELINI, P. (1994) 'About the level of daylight credit, speed of settlement and reserves in electronic payment systems', *Temi di discussione del servizio studi*, no 229, Banca d'Italia.

BELGISCHE VERENIGING DER BANKEN (1994) 'Grensoverschrijdende retailbetalingen. Voor een open en werkzame markt', *Aspecten en Documenten*, no 164, 25 p.

BORIO, C.E.V. & P. VAN DEN BERGH (1993) 'The Nature and Management of Payment System Risks: An International Perspective', *BIS Economic*

Papers, no 36, February, p. 8.

COMMITTEE OF EU CENTRAL BANK GOVERNORS (1993) *Minimum common features for domestic payment systems*, Report by the Working Group on EC Payment Systems, November.

MORTENSEN, J. (1994) *European Payment Systems and EMU*, CEPS Working Party Report no 11, Brussels, April, 97 p.

PADOA-SCHIOPPA, T. (1994) 'Central banking and payment systems in the European Community', *Economic Bulletin*, no 18, Banca d'Italia.

PINGITZER, J.C. and B.J. SUMMERS (1994) *Small-Value Transfer Systems*, in B.J. Summers (ed.), The Payment System. Design, Management, and Supervision, Washington D.C., International Monetary Fund, pp. 101-107.

RETAIL BANKING RESEARCH LTD. (1993) *Remote Cross-Border Payment Services*, Report for the Commission of the European Communities (DG XV), London, July.

RETAIL BANKING RESEARCH LTD. (1994) *Study in the Area of Payment Systems into the Transparency of Conditions for Remote Cross-Border Payment Services and the Performance of Cross-Border Transfers*, Report for the Commission of the European Communities (DG XV), London, August.

Index of Authors